Glencoe McGraw-Hill

Chapter 8 Resource Masters

Geometry

CONSUMABLE WORKBOOKS Many of the worksheets contained in the Chapter Resource Masters booklets are available as consumable workbooks in both English and Spanish.

	ISBN10	ISBN13
Study Guide and Intervention Workbook	0-07-890848-5	978-0-07-890848-4
Homework Practice Workbook	0-07-890849-3	978-0-07-890849-1
Spanish Version		
Homework Practice Workbook	0-07-890853-1	978-0-07-890853-8

ANSWERS FOR WORKBOOKS The answers for Chapter 8 of these workbooks can be found in the back of this Chapter Resource Masters booklet.

StudentWorks Plus™ This CD-ROM includes the entire Student Edition text along with the English workbooks listed above.

TeacherWorks Plus™ All of the materials found in this booklet are included for viewing, printing, and editing in this CD-ROM.

Spanish Assessment Masters (ISBN10: 0-07-890856-6, ISBN13: 978-0-07-890856-9)
These masters contain a Spanish version of Chapter 8 Test Form 2A and Form 2C.

The McGraw·Hill Companies

Send all inquiries to:
Glencoe/McGraw-Hill
8787 Orion Place
Columbus, OH 43240-4027

ISBN: 978-0-07-890517-9
MHID: 0-07-890517-6

Printed in the United States of America.

6 7 RHR 13 12

Contents

Teacher's Guide to Using the *Chapter 8 Resource Masters*

The *Chapter 8 Resource Masters* includes the core materials needed for Chapter 8. These materials include worksheets, extensions, and assessment options. The answers for these pages appear at the back of this booklet.

All of the materials found in this booklet are included for viewing and printing on the *TeacherWorks Plus™* CD-ROM.

Chapter Resources

Student-Built Glossary (pages 1–2) These masters are a student study tool that presents up to twenty of the key vocabulary terms from the chapter. Students are to record definitions and/or examples for each term. You may suggest that students highlight or star the terms with which they are not familiar. Give this to students before beginning Lesson 8-1. Encourage them to add these pages to their mathematics study notebooks. Remind them to complete the appropriate words as they study each lesson.

Anticipation Guide (pages 3–4) This master, presented in both English and Spanish, is a survey used before beginning the chapter to pinpoint what students may or may not know about the concepts in the chapter. Students will revisit this survey after they complete the chapter to see if their perceptions have changed.

Lesson Resources

Study Guide and Intervention These masters provide vocabulary, key concepts, additional worked-out examples and Check Your Progress exercises to use as a reteaching activity. It can also be used in conjunction with the Student Edition as an instructional tool for students who have been absent.

Skills Practice This master focuses more on the computational nature of the lesson. Use as an additional practice option or as homework for second-day teaching of the lesson.

Practice This master closely follows the types of problems found in the Exercises section of the Student Edition and includes word problems. Use as an additional practice option or as homework for second-day teaching of the lesson.

Word Problem Practice This master includes additional practice in solving word problems that apply the concepts of the lesson. Use as an additional practice or as homework for second-day teaching of the lesson.

Enrichment These activities may extend the concepts of the lesson, offer an historical or multicultural look at the concepts, or widen students' perspectives on the mathematics they are learning. They are written for use with all levels of students.

Graphing Calculator or Spreadsheet Activities
These activities present ways in which technology can be used with the concepts in some lessons of this chapter. Use as an alternative approach to some concepts or as an integral part of your lesson presentation.

Assessment Options

The assessment masters in the *Chapter 8 Resource Masters* offer a wide range of assessment tools for formative (monitoring) assessment and summative (final) assessment.

Student Recording Sheet This master corresponds with the standardized test practice at the end of the chapter.

Extended–Response Rubric This master provides information for teachers and students on how to assess performance on open-ended questions.

Quizzes Four free-response quizzes offer assessment at appropriate intervals in the chapter.

Mid-Chapter Test This 1-page test provides an option to assess the first half of the chapter. It parallels the timing of the Mid-Chapter Quiz in the Student Edition and includes both multiple-choice and free-response questions.

Vocabulary Test This test is suitable for all students. It includes a list of vocabulary words and 10 questions to assess students' knowledge of those words. This can also be used in conjunction with one of the leveled chapter tests.

Leveled Chapter Tests

- *Form 1* contains multiple-choice questions and is intended for use with below grade level students.
- *Forms 2A and 2B* contain multiple-choice questions aimed at on grade level students. These tests are similar in format to offer comparable testing situations.
- *Forms 2C and 2D* contain free-response questions aimed at on grade level students. These tests are similar in format to offer comparable testing situations.
- *Form 3* is a free-response test for use with above grade level students.

All of the above mentioned tests include a free-response Bonus question.

Extended-Response Test Performance assessment tasks are suitable for all students. Sample answers and a scoring rubric are included for evaluation.

Standardized Test Practice These three pages are cumulative in nature. It includes three parts: multiple-choice questions with bubble-in answer format, griddable questions with answer grids, and short-answer free-response questions.

Answers

- The answers for the Anticipation Guide and Lesson Resources are provided as reduced pages.
- Full-size answer keys are provided for the assessment masters.

8 Student-Built Glossary

This is an alphabetical list of the key vocabulary terms you will learn in Chapter 8. As you study the chapter, complete each term's definition or description. Remember to add the page number where you found the term. Add these pages to your Geometry Study Notebook to review vocabulary at the end of the chapter.

Vocabulary Term	Found on Page	Definition/Description/Example
angle of depression		
angle of elevation		
component form		
cosine		
geometric mean		
Law of Cosines		
Law of Sines		
magnitude		

(continued on the next page)

NAME ______________________ DATE ____________ PERIOD ____________

8 Student-Built Glossary *(continued)*

Vocabulary Term	Found on Page	Definition/Description/Example
Pythagorean triple		
resultant		
sine		
tangent		
trigonometric ratio		
trigonometry		
vector		

8-1 Study Guide and Intervention

Geometric Mean

Geometric Mean The **geometric mean** between two numbers is the positive square root of their product. For two positive numbers a and b, the geometric mean of a and b is the positive number x in the proportion $\frac{a}{x} = \frac{x}{b}$. Cross multiplying gives $x^2 = ab$, so $x = \sqrt{ab}$.

Example **Find the geometric mean between each pair of numbers.**

a. 12 and 3

$x = \sqrt{ab}$	Definition of geometric mean
$= \sqrt{12 \cdot 3}$	$a = 12$ and $b = 3$
$= \sqrt{(2 \cdot 2 \cdot 3) \cdot 3}$	Factor.
$= 6$	Simplify.

The geometric mean between 12 and 3 is 6.

b. 8 and 4

$x = \sqrt{ab}$	Definition of geometric mean
$= \sqrt{8 \cdot 4}$	$a = 8$ and $b = 4$
$= \sqrt{(2 \cdot 4) \cdot 4}$	Factor.
$= \sqrt{16 \cdot 2}$	Associative Property
$= 4\sqrt{2}$	Simplify.

The geometric mean between 8 and 4 is $4\sqrt{2}$ or about 5.7.

Lesson 8-1

Exercises

Find the geometric mean between each pair of numbers.

1. 4 and 4

2. 4 and 6

3. 6 and 9

4. $\frac{1}{2}$ and 2

5. 12 and 20

6. 4 and 25

7. 16 and 30

8. 10 and 100

9. $\frac{1}{2}$ and $\frac{1}{4}$

10. 17 and 3

11. 4 and 16

12. 3 and 24

NAME ______________________ DATE ____________ PERIOD ____________

8-1 Study Guide and Intervention *(continued)*

Geometric Mean

Geometric Means in Right Triangles In the diagram, $\triangle ABC \sim \triangle ADB \sim \triangle BDC$. An altitude to the hypotenuse of a right triangle forms two right triangles. The two triangles are similar and each is similar to the original triangle.

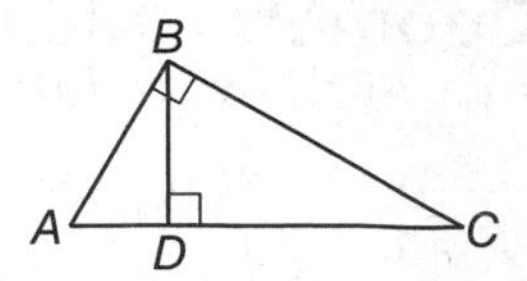

Example 1 **Use right $\triangle ABC$ with $\overline{BD} \perp \overline{AC}$. Describe two geometric means.**

a. $\triangle ADB \sim \triangle BDC$ so $\frac{AD}{BD} = \frac{BD}{CD}$.

In $\triangle ABC$, the altitude is the geometric mean between the two segments of the hypotenuse.

b. $\triangle ABC \sim \triangle ADB$ and $\triangle ABC \sim \triangle BDC$, so $\frac{AC}{AB} = \frac{AB}{AD}$ and $\frac{AC}{BC} = \frac{BC}{DC}$.

In $\triangle ABC$, each leg is the geometric mean between the hypotenuse and the segment of the hypotenuse adjacent to that leg.

Example 2 **Find x, y, and z.**

$15 = \sqrt{RP \cdot SP}$ Geometric Mean (Leg) Theorem

$15 = \sqrt{25x}$ $RP = 25$ and $SP = x$

$225 = 25x$ Square each side.

$9 = x$ Divide each side by 25.

Then

$y = RP - SP$

$= 25 - 9$

$= 16$

$z = \sqrt{RS \cdot RP}$ Geometric Mean (Leg) Theorem

$= \sqrt{16 \cdot 25}$ $RS = 16$ and $RP = 25$

$= \sqrt{400}$ Multiply.

$= 20$ Simplify.

Exercises

Find x, y, and z to the nearest tenth.

1.

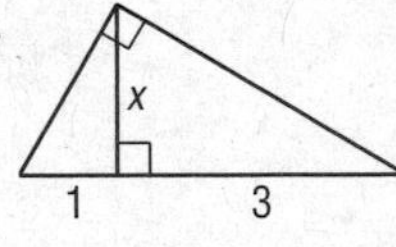

2.

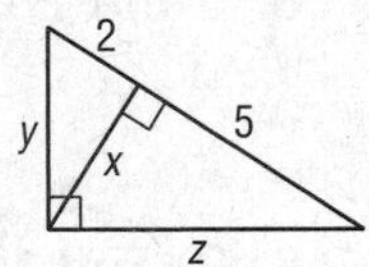

3.

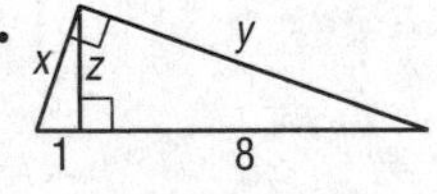

4.

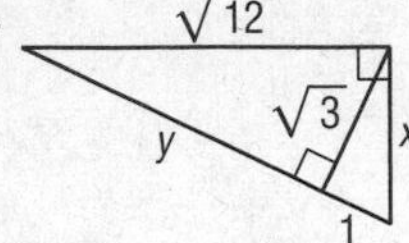

5.

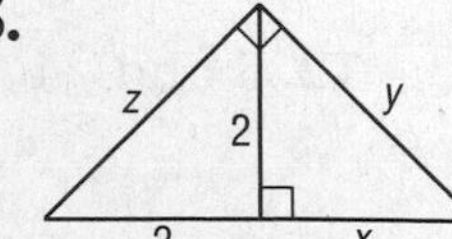

6.

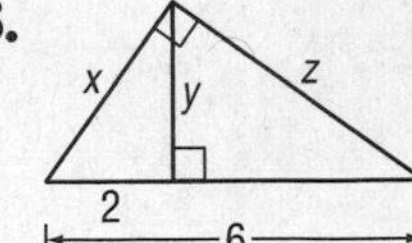

NAME ______________________ DATE ____________ PERIOD ____________

8-1 Skills Practice

Geometric Mean

Find the geometric mean between each pair of numbers.

1. 2 and 8

2. 9 and 36

3. 4 and 7

4. 5 and 10

5. 28 and 14

6. 7 and 36

Write a similarity statement identifying the three similar triangles in the figure.

7.

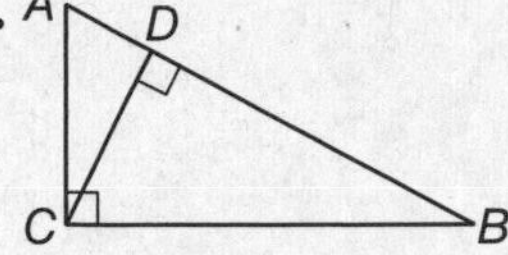

8.

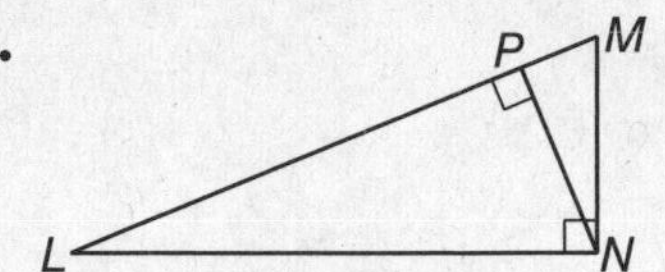

9.

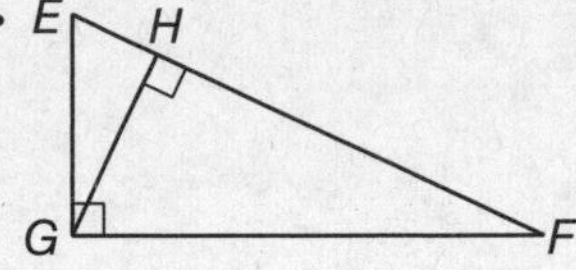

10.

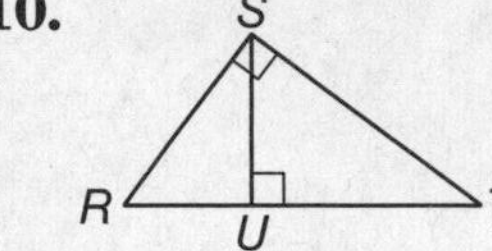

Find x, y and z.

11.

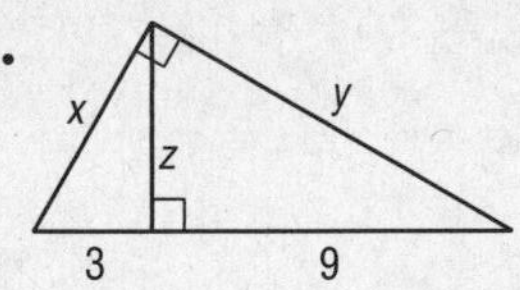

12.

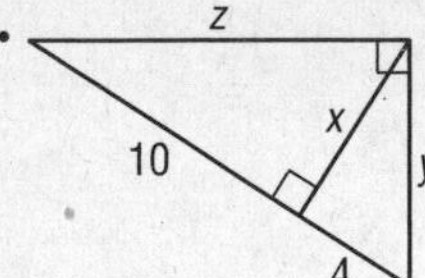

13.

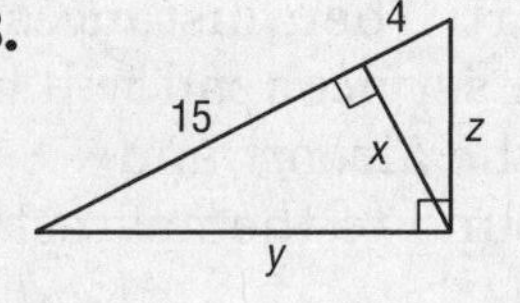

14.

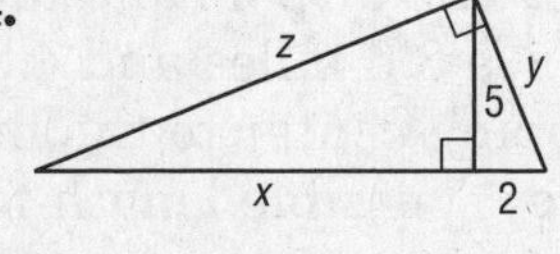

Lesson 8-1

NAME ______________________ DATE ____________ PERIOD ____________

8-1 Practice

Geometric Mean

Find the geometric mean between each pair of numbers.

1. 8 and 12

2. 3 and 15

3. $\frac{4}{5}$ and 2

Write a similarity statement identifying the three similar triangles in the figure.

4.

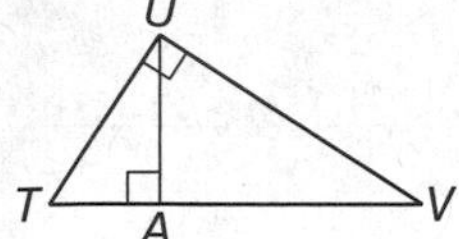

5.

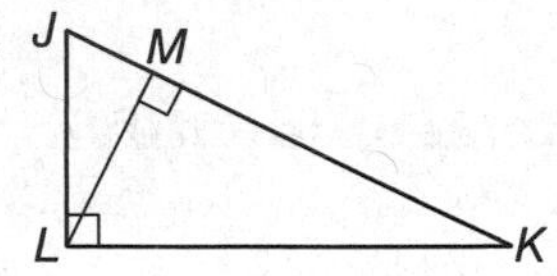

Find *x*, *y*, and *z*.

6.

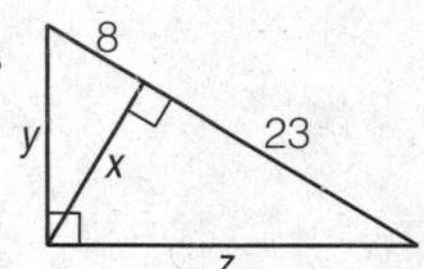

7.

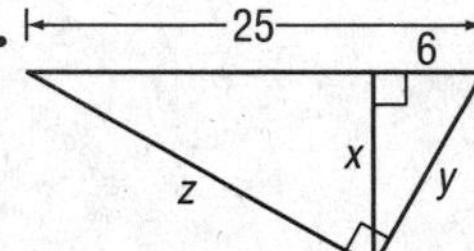

8.

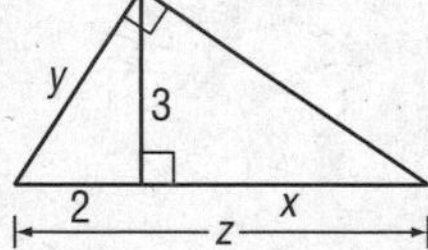

9.

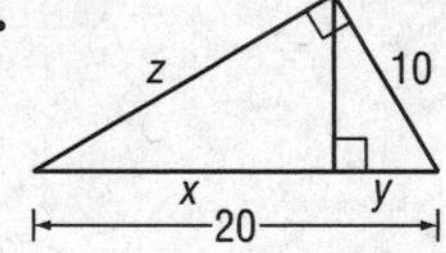

10. CIVIL An airport, a factory, and a shopping center are at the vertices of a right triangle formed by three highways. The airport and factory are 6.0 miles apart. Their distances from the shopping center are 3.6 miles and 4.8 miles, respectively. A service road will be constructed from the shopping center to the highway that connects the airport and factory. What is the shortest possible length for the service road? Round to the nearest hundredth.

NAME ______________________ DATE __________ PERIOD __________

8-1 Word Problem Practice

Geometric Mean

1. **SQUARES** Wilma has a rectangle of dimensions ℓ by w. She would like to replace it with a square that has the same area. What is the side length of the square with the same area as Wilma's rectangle?

2. **EQUALITY** Gretchen computed the geometric mean of two numbers. One of the numbers was 7 and the geometric mean turned out to be 7 as well. What was the other number?

3. **VIEWING ANGLE** A photographer wants to take a picture of a beach front. His camera has a viewing angle of 90° and he wants to make sure two palm trees located at points A and B in the figure are just inside the edges of the photograph.

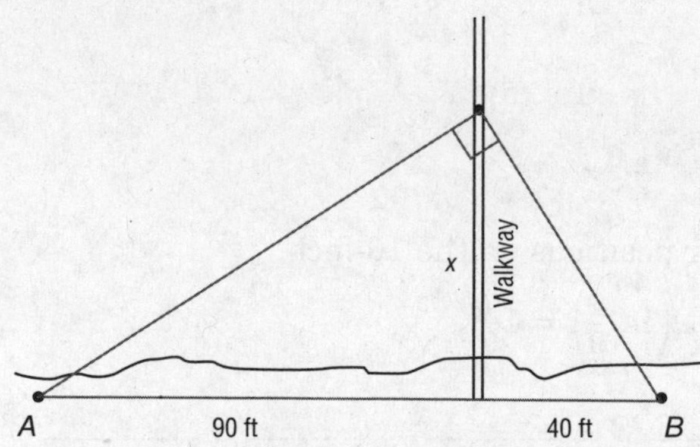

He walks out on a walkway that goes over the ocean to get the shot. If his camera has a viewing angle of 90°, at what distance down the walkway should he stop to take his photograph?

4. **EXHIBITIONS** A museum has a famous statue on display. The curator places the statue in the corner of a rectangular room and builds a 15-foot-long railing in front of the statue. Use the information below to find how close visitors will be able to get to the statue.

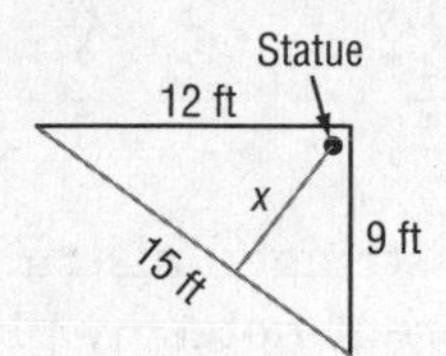

5. **CLIFFS** A bridge connects to a tunnel as shown in the figure. The bridge is 180 feet above the ground. At a distance of 235 feet along the bridge out of the tunnel, the angle to the base and summit of the cliff is a right angle.

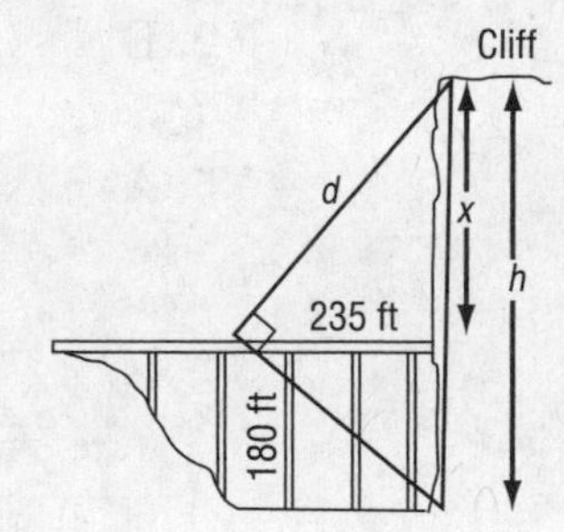

a. What is the height of the cliff? Round to the nearest whole number.

b. How high is the cliff from base to summit? Round to the nearest whole number.

c. What is the value of d? Round to the nearest whole number.

Lesson 8-1

NAME ______________________ DATE __________ PERIOD __________

8-1 Enrichment

Mathematics and Music

Pythagoras, a Greek philosopher who lived during the sixth century B.C., believed that all nature, beauty, and harmony could be expressed by whole-number relationships. Most people remember Pythagoras for his teachings about right triangles. (The sum of the squares of the legs equals the square of the hypotenuse.) But Pythagoras also discovered relationships between the musical notes of a scale. These relationships can be expressed as ratios.

C	D	E	F	G	A	B	C′
$\frac{1}{1}$	$\frac{8}{9}$	$\frac{4}{5}$	$\frac{3}{4}$	$\frac{2}{3}$	$\frac{3}{5}$	$\frac{8}{15}$	$\frac{1}{2}$

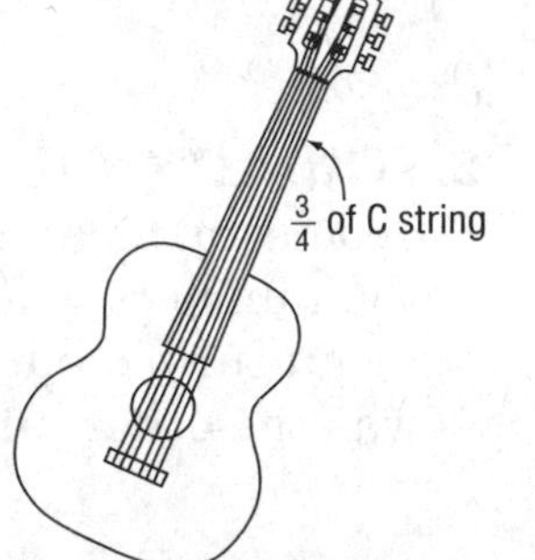

When you play a stringed instrument, you produce different notes by placing your finger on different places on a string. This is the result of changing the length of the vibrating part of the string.

The C string can be used to produce F by placing a finger $\frac{3}{4}$ of the way along the string.

Suppose a C string has a length of 16 inches. Write and solve proportions to determine what length of string would have to vibrate to produce the remaining notes of the scale.

1. D

2. E

3. F

4. G

5. A

6. B

7. C′

8. Complete to show the distance between finger positions on the 16-inch C string for each note. For example, $C(16) - D\left(14\frac{2}{9}\right) = 1\frac{7}{9}$.

C $1\frac{7}{9}$ in. D ________ E ________ F ________ G ________ A ________ B ________ C′

8-2 Study Guide and Intervention

The Pythagorean Theorem and Its Converse

The Pythagorean Theorem In a right triangle, the sum of the squares of the lengths of the legs equals the square of the length of the hypotenuse. If the three whole numbers a, b, and c satisfy the equation $a^2 + b^2 = c^2$, then the numbers a, b, and c form a **Pythagorean triple.**

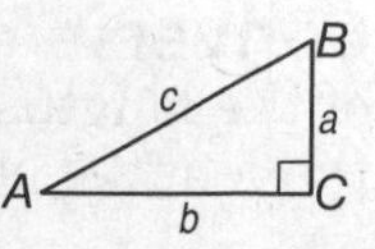

$\triangle ABC$ is a right triangle.

so $a^2 + b^2 = c^2$.

Example

a. Find a.

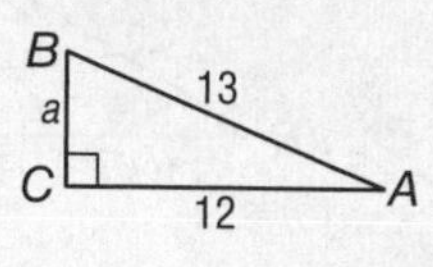

$a^2 + b^2 = c^2$	Pythagorean Theorem
$a^2 + 12^2 = 13^2$	$b = 12$, $c = 13$
$a^2 + 144 = 169$	Simplify.
$a^2 = 25$	Subtract.
$a = 5$	Take the positive square root of each side.

b. Find c.

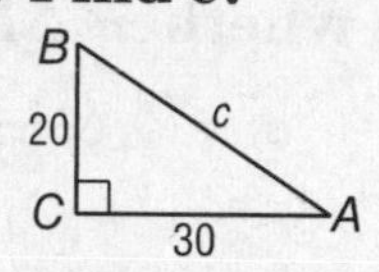

$a^2 + b^2 = c^2$	Pythagorean Theorem
$20^2 + 30^2 = c^2$	$a = 20$, $b = 30$
$400 + 900 = c^2$	Simplify.
$1300 = c^2$	Add.
$\sqrt{1300} = c$	Take the positive square root of each side.
$36.1 \approx c$	Use a calculator.

Exercises

Find x.

1.

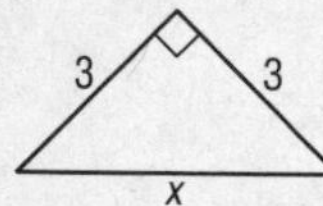

2.

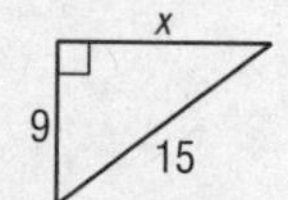

3.

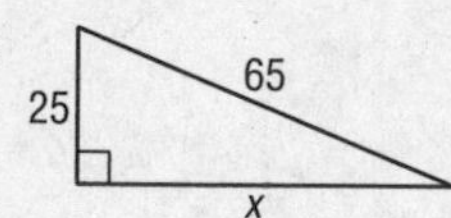

4.

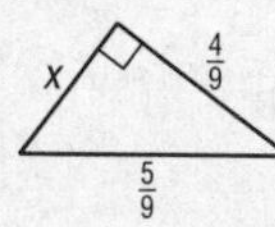

5.

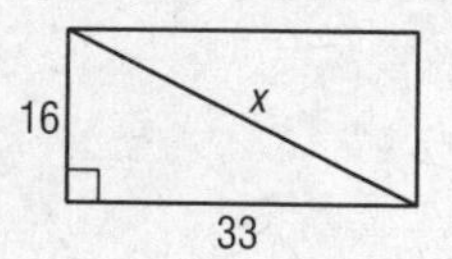

6.

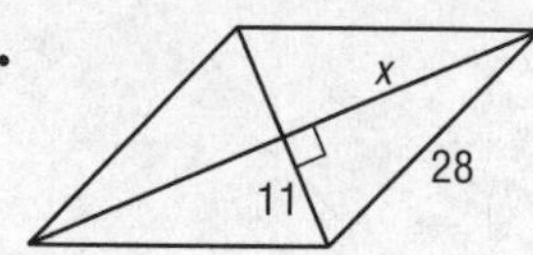

Use a Pythagorean Triple to find x.

7.

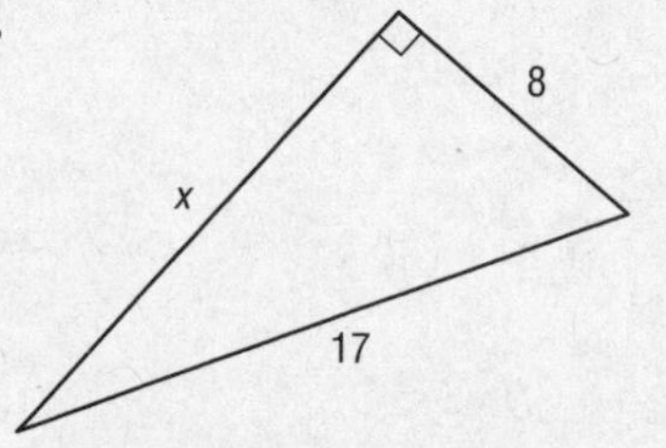

8.

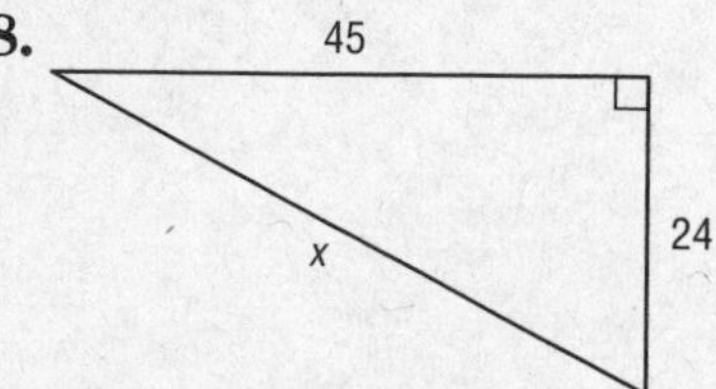

9.

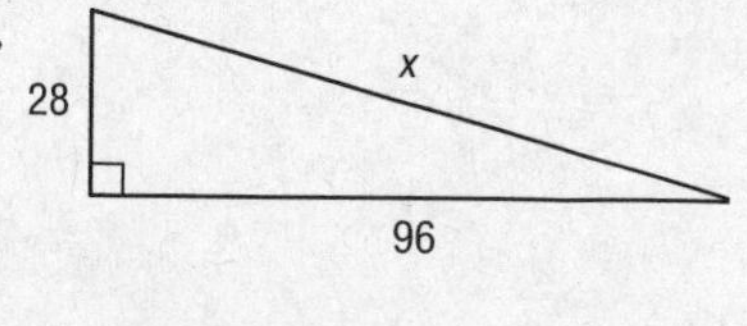

NAME ______________________ DATE ____________ PERIOD ____________

8-2 Study Guide and Intervention *(continued)*

The Pythagorean Theorem and Its Converse

Converse of the Pythagorean Theorem If the sum of the squares of the lengths of the two shorter sides of a triangle equals the square of the lengths of the longest side, then the triangle is a right triangle.

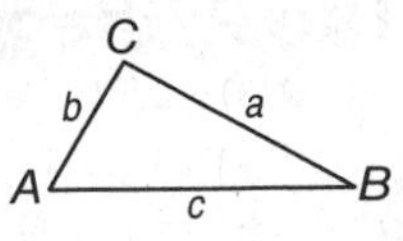

If $a^2 + b^2 = c^2$, then $\triangle ABC$ is a right triangle.

You can also use the lengths of sides to classify a triangle.

if $a^2 + b^2 = c^2$ then $\triangle ABC$ is a right triangle.
if $a^2 + b^2 > c^2$ then $\triangle ABC$ is acute.
if $a^2 + b^2 < c^2$ then $\triangle ABC$ is obtuse.

Example **Determine whether $\triangle PQR$ is a right triangle.**

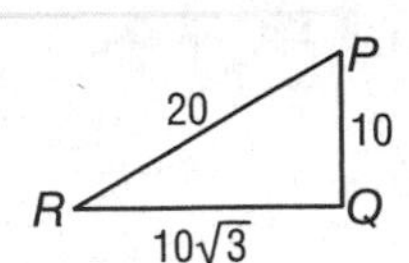

$a^2 + b^2 \stackrel{?}{=} c^2$	Compare c^2 and $a^2 + b^2$
$10^2 + (10\sqrt{3})^2 \stackrel{?}{=} 20^2$	$a = 10$, $b = 10\sqrt{3}$, $c = 20$
$100 + 300 \stackrel{?}{=} 400$	Simplify.
$400 = 400$ ✓	Add.

Since $c^2 =$ and $a^2 + b^2$, the triangle is a right triangle.

Exercises

Determine whether each set of measures can be the measures of the sides of a triangle. If so, classify the triangle as *acute*, *obtuse*, or *right*. Justify your answer.

1. 30, 40, 50

2. 20, 30, 40

3. 18, 24, 30

4. 6, 8, 9

5. 6, 12, 18

6. 10, 15, 20

7. $\sqrt{5}$, $\sqrt{12}$, $\sqrt{13}$

8. 2, $\sqrt{8}$, $\sqrt{12}$

9. 9, 40, 41

NAME ______________________ DATE __________ PERIOD __________

8-2 Skills Practice

The Pythagorean Theorem and Its Converse

Find x.

1.

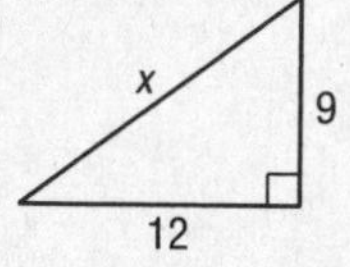

2.

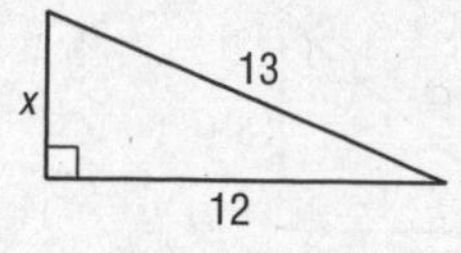

3.

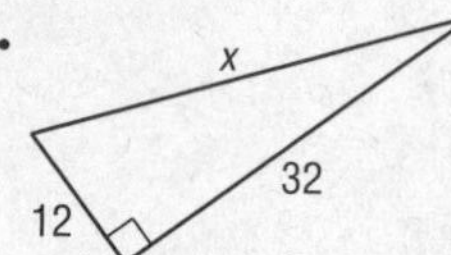

4.

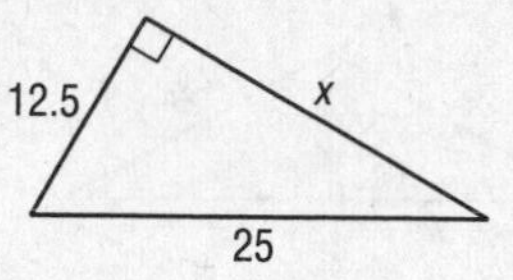

5.

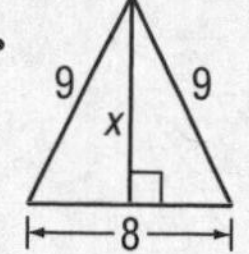

6.

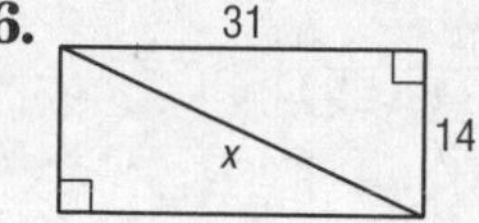

Use a Pythagorean Triple to find x.

7.

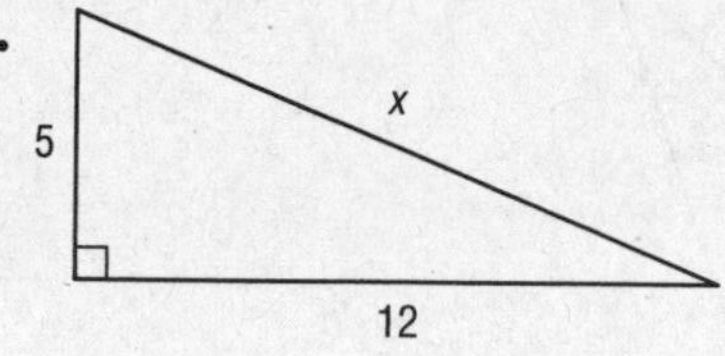

8.

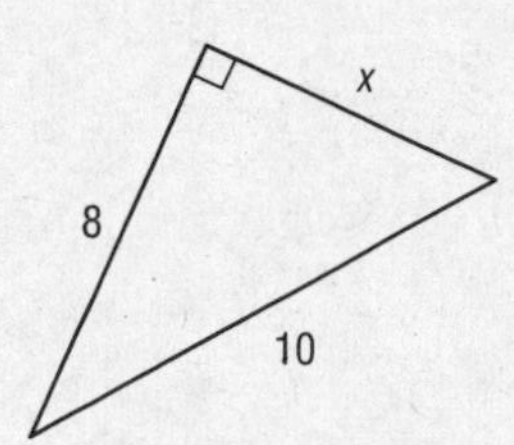

9.

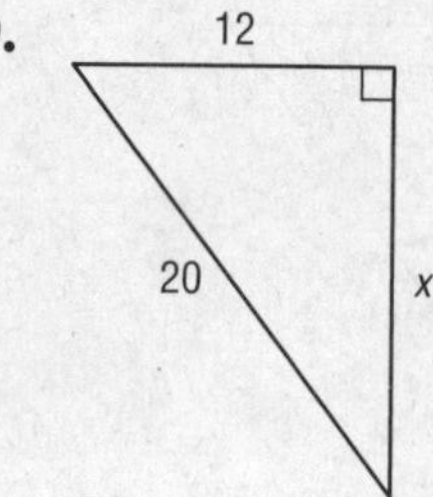

10.

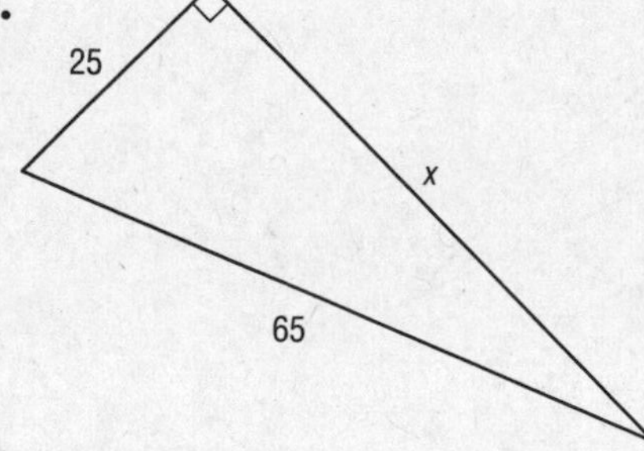

11.

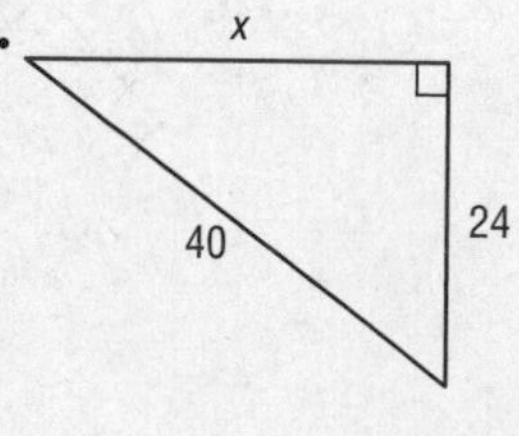

12.

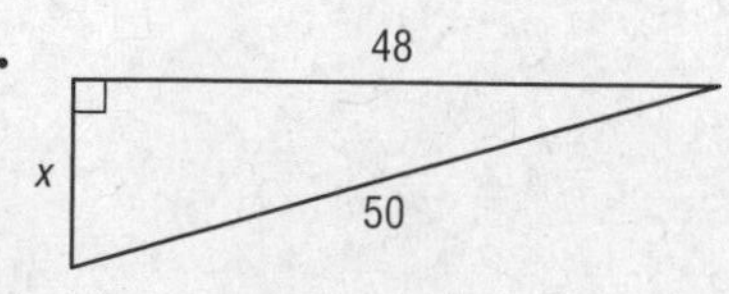

Determine whether each set of numbers can be measure of the sides of a triangle. If so, classify the triangle as *acute, obtuse, or right*. Justify your answer.

13. 7, 24, 25

14. 8, 14, 20

15. 12.5, 13, 26

16. $3\sqrt{2}$, $\sqrt{7}$, 4

17. 20, 21, 29

18. 32, 35, 70

Lesson 8-2

NAME ______________________ DATE ____________ PERIOD ____________

8-2 Practice

The Pythagorean Theorem and Its Converse

Find x.

1.

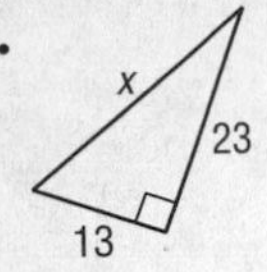

2.

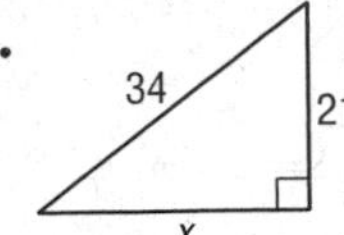

3.

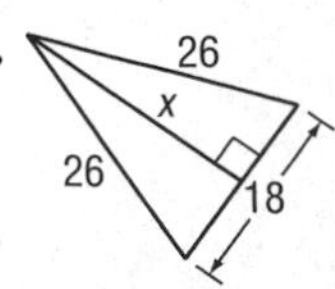

4.

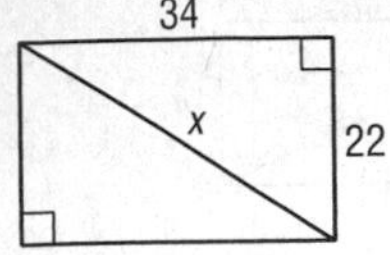

5.

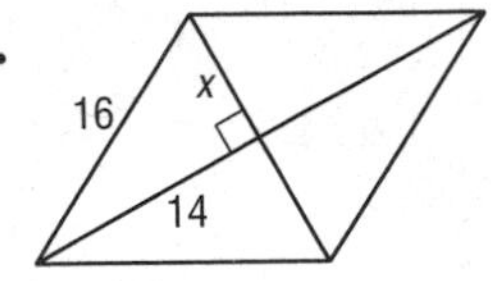

6.

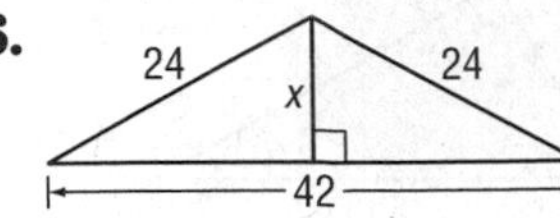

Use a Pythagorean Triple to find x.

7.

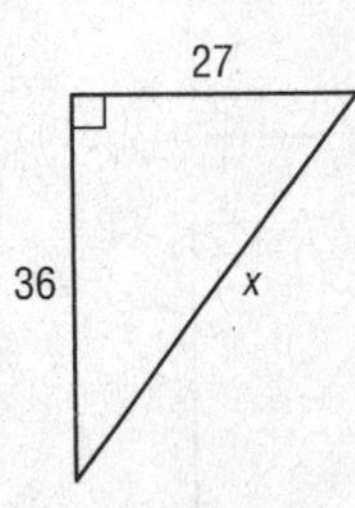

8.

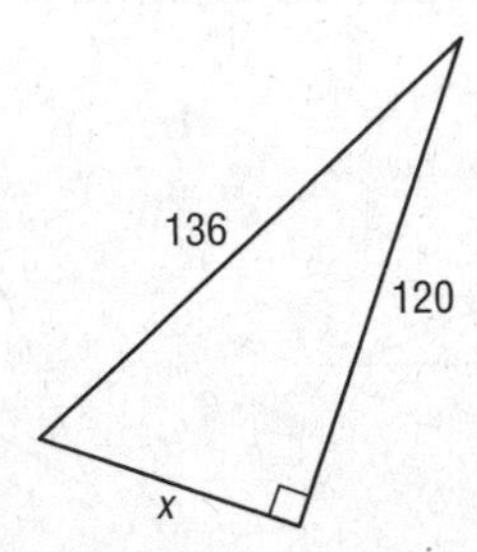

9.

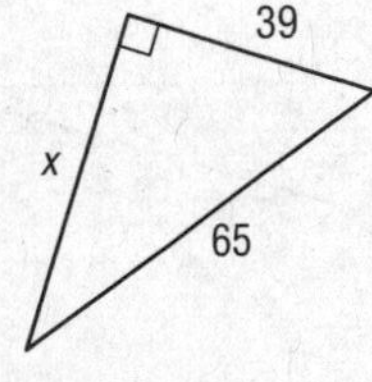

10.

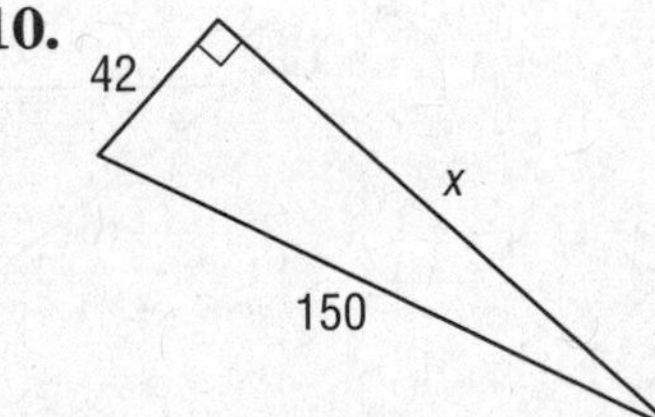

Determine whether each set of numbers can be measure of the sides of a triangle. If so, classify the triangle as *acute, obtuse, or right*. Justify your answer.

11. 10, 11, 20

12. 12, 14, 49

13. $5\sqrt{2}$, 10, 11

14. 21.5, 24, 55.5

15. 30, 40, 50

16. 65, 72, 97

17. CONSTRUCTION The bottom end of a ramp at a warehouse is 10 feet from the base of the main dock and is 11 feet long. How high is the dock?

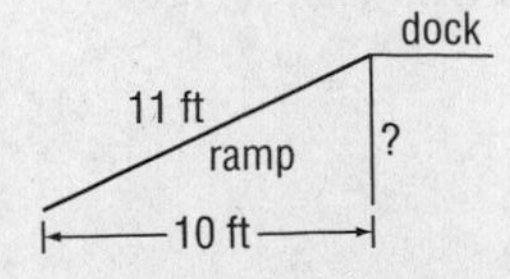

NAME ______________________ DATE ____________ PERIOD ____________

8-2 Word Problem Practice

The Pythagorean Theorem and Its Converse

1. **SIDEWALKS** Construction workers are building a marble sidewalk around a park that is shaped like a right triangle. Each marble slab adds 2 feet to the length of the sidewalk. The workers find that exactly 1071 and 1840 slabs are required to make the sidewalks along the short sides of the park. How many slabs are required to make the sidewalk that runs along the long side of the park?

2. **RIGHT ANGLES** Clyde makes a triangle using three sticks of lengths 20 inches, 21 inches, and 28 inches. Is the triangle a right triangle? Explain.

3. **TETHERS** To help support a flag pole, a 50-foot-long tether is tied to the pole at a point 40 feet above the ground. The tether is pulled taut and tied to an anchor in the ground. How far away from the base of the pole is the anchor?

4. **FLIGHT** An airplane lands at an airport 60 miles east and 25 miles north of where it took off.

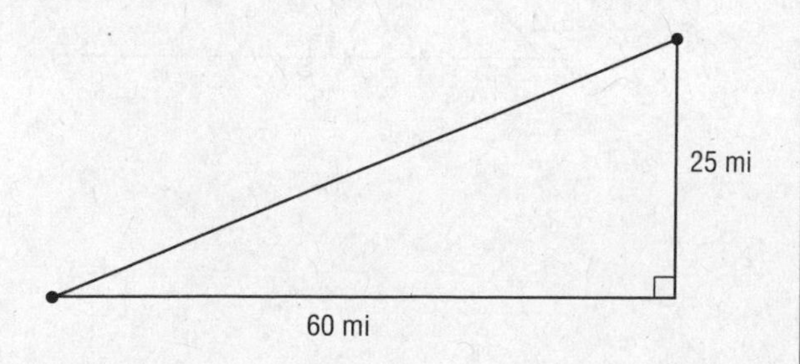

How far apart are the two airports?

5. **PYTHAGOREAN TRIPLES** Ms. Jones assigned her fifth-period geometry class the following problem.
Let m and n be two positive integers with $m > n$. Let $a = m^2 - n^2$, $b = 2mn$, and $c = m^2 + n^2$.

 a. Show that there is a right triangle with side lengths a, b, and c.

 b. Complete the following table.

m	n	a	b	c
2	1	3	4	5
3	1			
3	2			
4	1			
4	2			
4	3			
5	1			

 c. Find a Pythagorean triple that corresponds to a right triangle with a hypotenuse $25^2 = 625$ units long. (*Hint:* Use the table you completed for Exercise b to find two positive integers m and n with $m > n$ and $m^2 + n^2 = 625$.)

Lesson 8-2

8-2 Enrichment

Converse of a Right Triangle Theorem

You have learned that the measure of the altitude from the vertex of the right angle of a right triangle to its hypotenuse is the geometric mean between the measures of the two segments of the hypotenuse. Is the converse of this theorem true? In order to find out, it will help to rewrite the original theorem in if-then form as follows.

If $\triangle ABQ$ is a right triangle with right angle at Q, then QP is the geometric mean between AP and PB, where P is between A and B and $\overline{QP}$ is perpendicular to $\overline{AB}$.

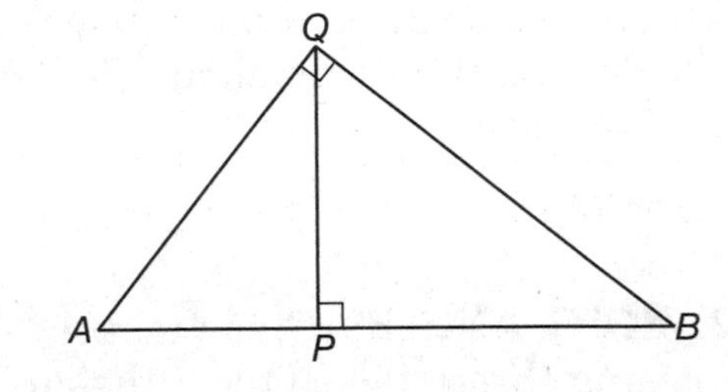

1. Write the converse of the if-then form of the theorem.

2. Is the converse of the original theorem true? Refer to the figure at the right to explain your answer.

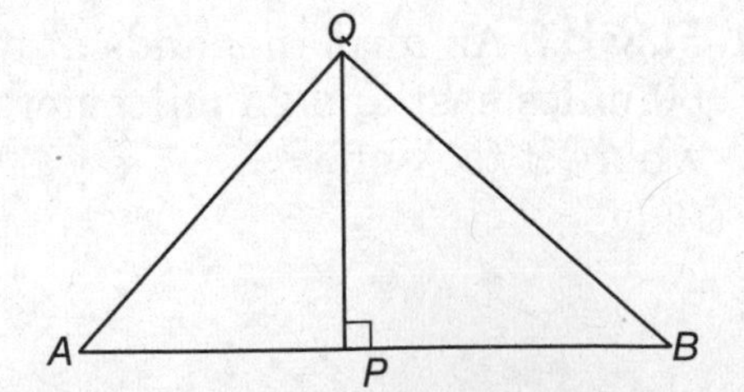

You may find it interesting to examine the other theorems in Chapter 8 to see whether their converses are true or false. You will need to restate the theorems carefully in order to write their converses.

NAME ______________________ DATE ____________ PERIOD ____________

8-2 Spreadsheet Activity

Pythagorean Triples

You can use a spreadsheet to determine whether three whole numbers form a Pythagorean triple.

Example 1 **Use a spreadsheet to determine whether the numbers 12, 16, and 20 form a Pythagorean triple.**

Step 1 In cell A1, enter 12. In cell B1, enter 16 and in cell C1, enter 20. *The longest side should be entered in column C.*

Step 2 In cell D1, enter an equals sign followed by IF(A1^2+B1^2=C1^2,"YES","NO"). This will return "YES" if the set of numbers is a Pythagorean triple and will return "NO" if it is not.

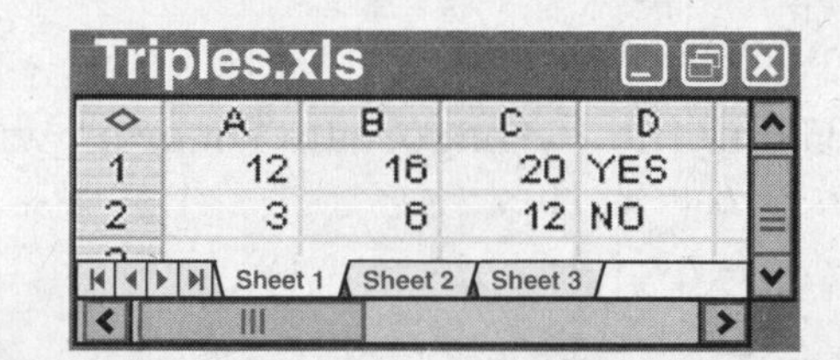

Triples.xls
A
B
C
D
1
12
16
20
YES
2
3
6
12
NO
Sheet 1
Sheet 2
Sheet 3

The numbers 12, 16, and 20 form a Pythagorean triple.

Example 2 **Use a spreadsheet to determine whether the numbers 3, 6, and 12 form a Pythagorean triple.**

Step 1 In cell A2, enter 3, in cell B2, enter 6, and in cell C2, enter 12.

Step 2 Click on the bottom right corner of cell D1 and drag it to D2. This will determine whether or not the set of numbers is a Pythagorean triple.

The numbers 3, 6, and 12 do not form a Pythagorean triple.

Exercises

Use a spreadsheet to determine whether each set of numbers forms a Pythagorean triple.

1. 14, 48, 50

2. 16, 30, 34

3. 5, 5, 9

4. 4, 5, 7

5. 18, 24, 30

6. 10, 24, 26

7. 25, 60, 65

8. 2, 4, 5

9. 19, 21, 22

10. 18, 80, 82

11. 5, 12, 13

12. 20, 48, 52

Lesson 8-2

8-3 Study Guide and Intervention

Special Right Triangles

Properties of 45°-45°-90° Triangles The sides of a 45°-45°-90° right triangle have a special relationship.

Example 1 **If the leg of a 45°-45°-90° right triangle is x units, show that the hypotenuse is $x\sqrt{2}$ units.**

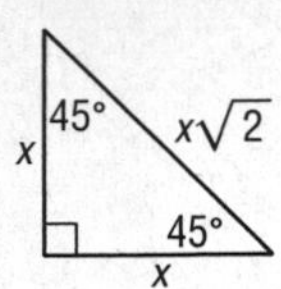

Using the Pythagorean Theorem with $a = b = x$, then

$c^2 = a^2 + b^2$

$c^2 = x^2 + x^2$

$c^2 = 2x^2$

$c = \sqrt{2x^2}$

$c = x\sqrt{2}$

Example 2 **In a 45°-45°-90° right triangle the hypotenuse is $\sqrt{2}$ times the leg. If the hypotenuse is 6 units, find the length of each leg.**

The hypotenuse is $\sqrt{2}$ times the leg, so divide the length of the hypotenuse by $\sqrt{2}$.

$$a = \frac{6}{\sqrt{2}}$$

$$= \frac{6}{\sqrt{2}} \cdot \frac{\sqrt{2}}{\sqrt{2}}$$

$$= \frac{6\sqrt{2}}{2}$$

$$= 3\sqrt{2} \text{ units}$$

Exercises

Find x.

1. 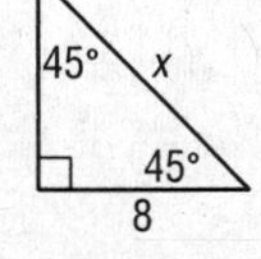

2. 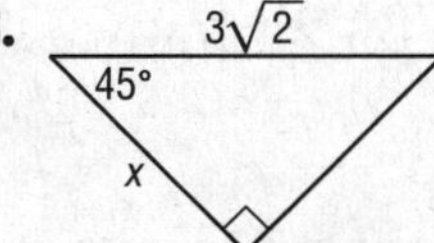

3. 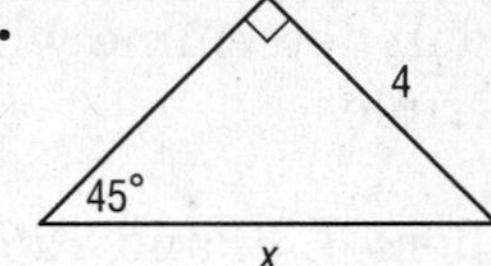

4. 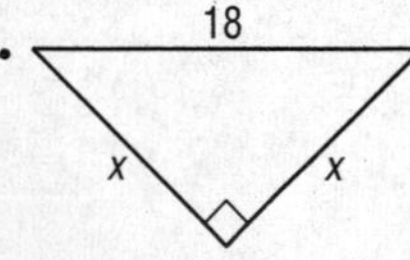

5. 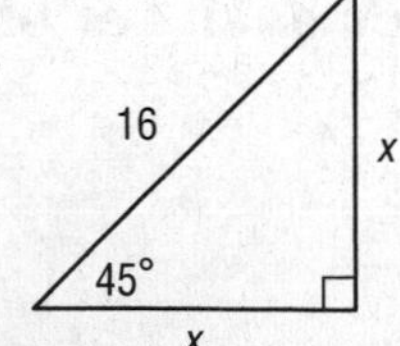

6. 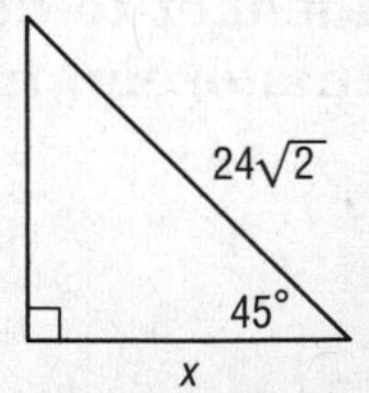

7. If a 45°-45°-90° triangle has a hypotenuse length of 12, find the leg length.

8. Determine the length of the leg of 45°-45°-90° triangle with a hypotenuse length of 25 inches.

9. Find the length of the hypotenuse of a 45°-45°-90° triangle with a leg length of 14 centimeters.

NAME ______________________ DATE ____________ PERIOD ____________

8-3 Study Guide and Intervention *(continued)*

Special Right Triangles

Properties of 30°-60°-90° Triangles The sides of a 30°-60°-90° right triangle also have a special relationship.

Example 1 **In a 30°-60°-90° right triangle the hypotenuse is twice the shorter leg. Show that the longer leg is $\sqrt{3}$ times the shorter leg.**

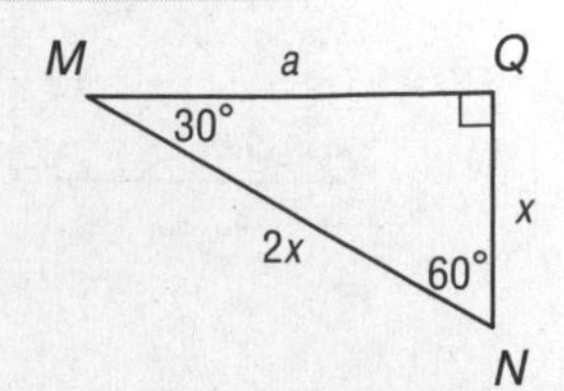

$\triangle MNQ$ is a 30°-60°-90° right triangle, and the length of the hypotenuse $\overline{MN}$ is two times the length of the shorter side $\overline{NQ}$.
Use the Pythagorean Theorem.

$a^2 = (2x)^2 - x^2$ — $a^2 = c^2 - b^2$

$a^2 = 4x^2 - x^2$ — Multiply.

$a^2 = 3x^2$ — Subtract.

$a = \sqrt{3x^2}$ — Take the positive square root of each side.

$a = x\sqrt{3}$ — Simplify.

Example 2 **In a 30°-60°-90° right triangle, the hypotenuse is 5 centimeters. Find the lengths of the other two sides of the triangle.**

If the hypotenuse of a 30°-60°-90° right triangle is 5 centimeters, then the length of the shorter leg is one-half of 5, or 2.5 centimeters. The length of the longer leg is $\sqrt{3}$ times the length of the shorter leg, or $(2.5)(\sqrt{3})$ centimeters.

Exercises

Find *x* and *y*.

1.

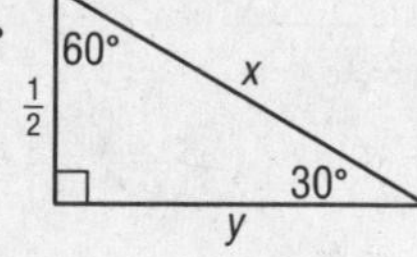

2.

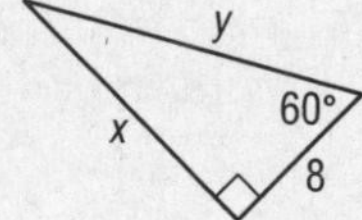

3.

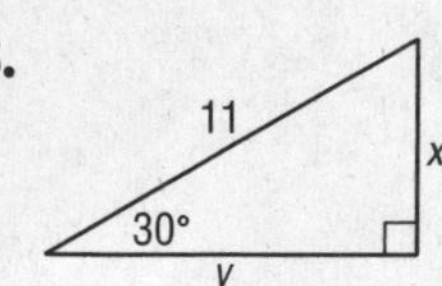

4.

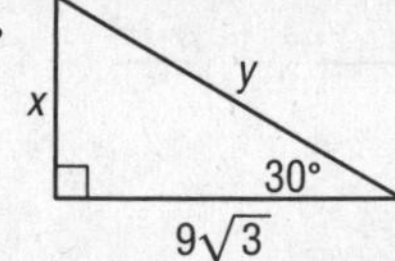

5.

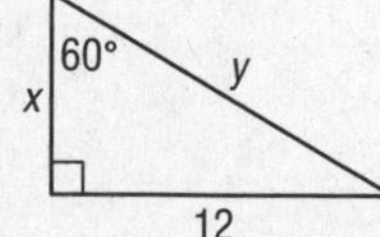

6.

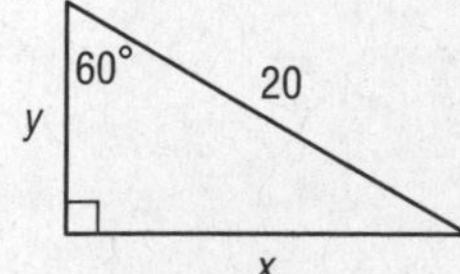

7. An equilateral triangle has an altitude length of 36 feet. Determine the length of a
of the triangle.

8. Find the length of the side of an equilateral triangle that has an altitud
45 centimeters.

NAME ______________________________ DATE ____________ PERIOD ____________

8-3 Skills Practice

Special Right Triangles

Find x.

1.

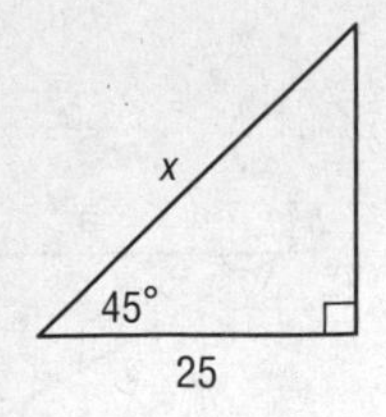

2.

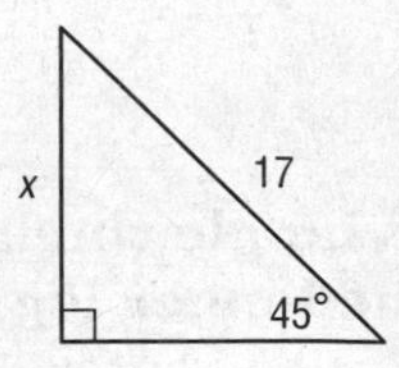

3.

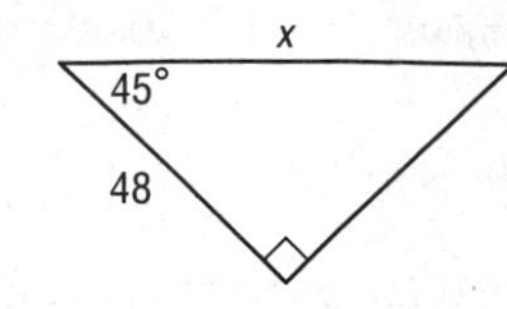

4.

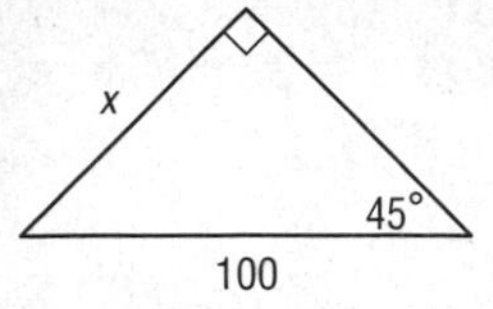

5.

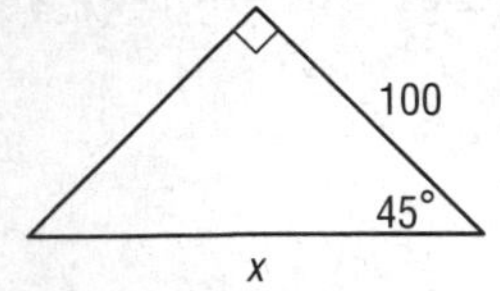

6.

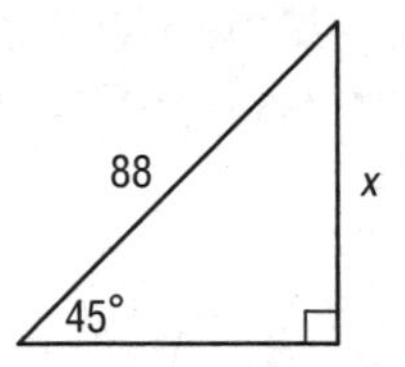

7. Determine the length of the leg of 45°-45°-90° triangle with a hypotenuse length of 26.

8. Find the length of the hypotenuse of a 45°-45°-90° triangle with a leg length of 50 centimeters.

Find x and y.

9.

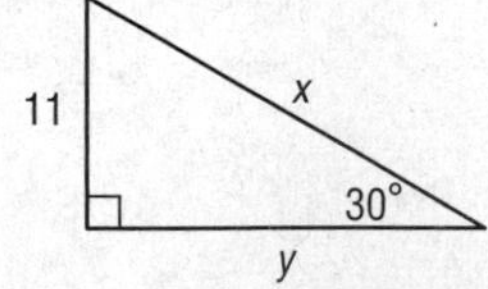

10.

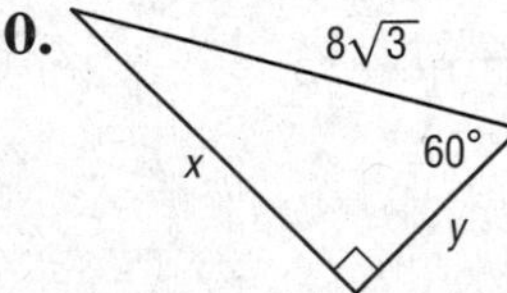

11.

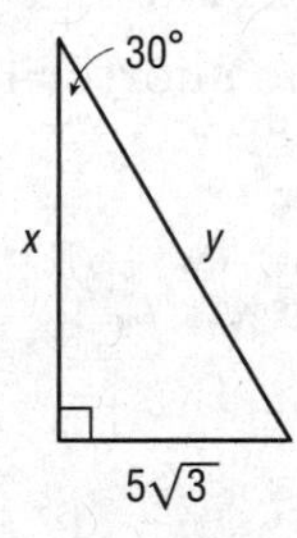

12.

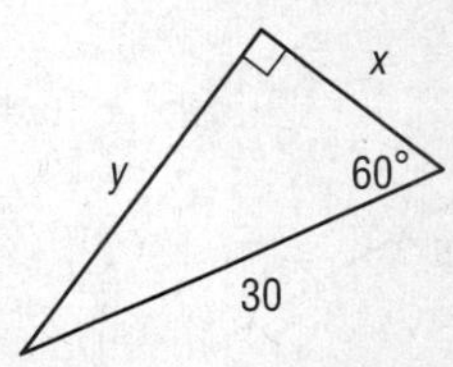

13.

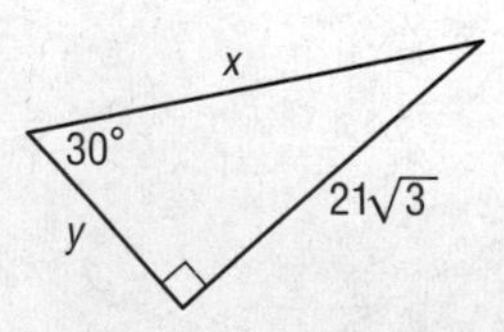

14.

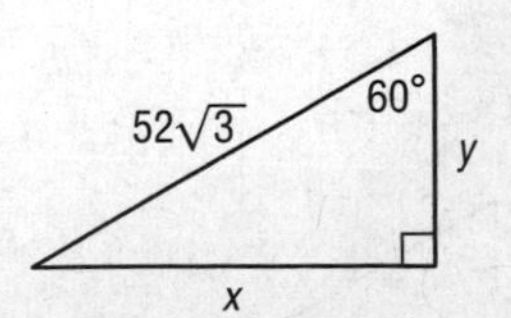

15. An equilateral triangle has an altitude length of 27 feet. Determine the length of a side of the triangle.

6. Find the length of the side of an equilateral triangle that has an altitude length of $11\sqrt{3}$ feet.

NAME ______________________ DATE ____________ PERIOD ____________

8-3 Practice

Special Right Triangles

Find x.

1.

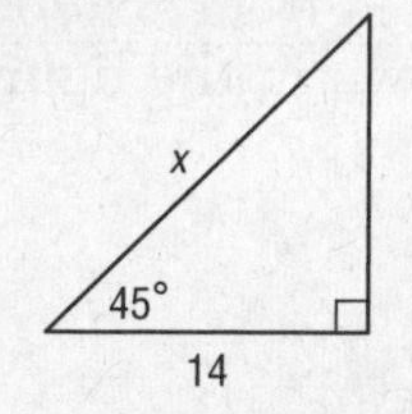

2.

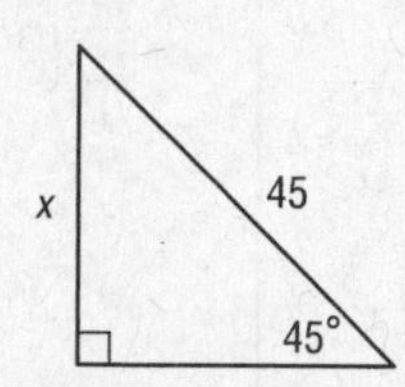

3.

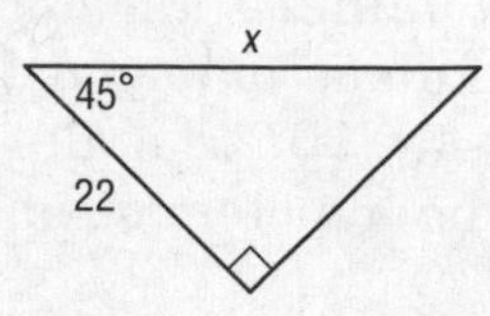

4.

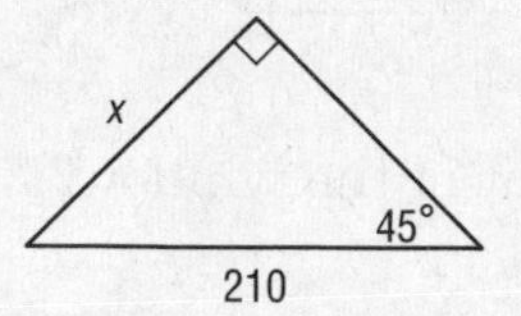

5.

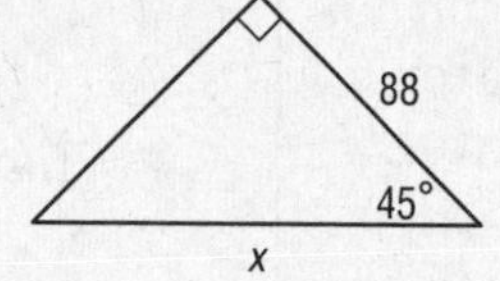

6.

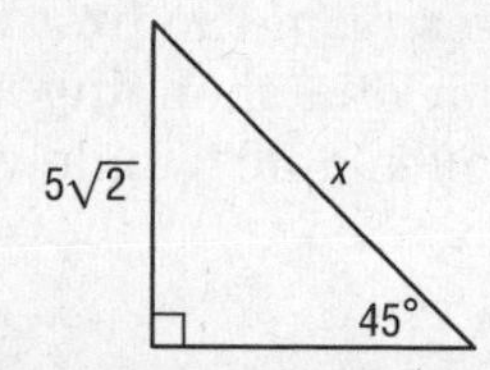

Find x and y.

7.

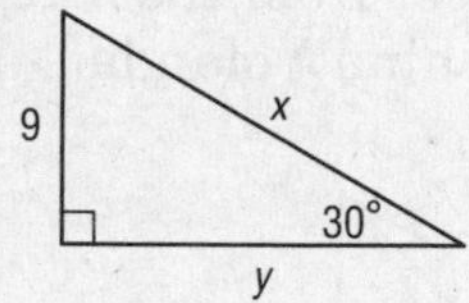

8.

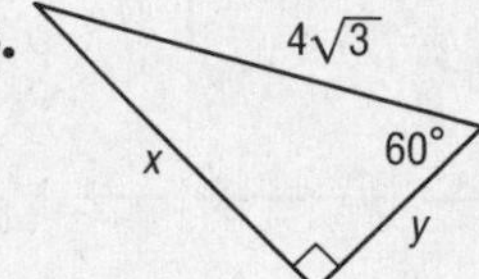

9.

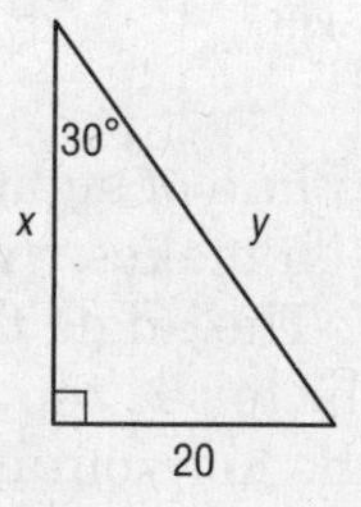

10.

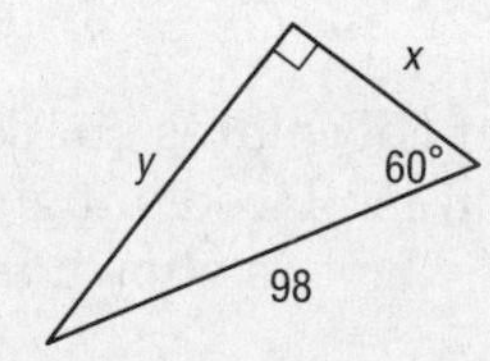

11. Determine the length of the leg of 45°-45°-90° triangle with a hypotenuse length of 38.

12. Find the length of the hypotenuse of a 45°-45°-90° triangle with a leg length of 77 centimeters.

13. An equilateral triangle has an altitude length of 33 feet. Determine the length of a side of the triangle.

14. BOTANICAL GARDENS One of the displays at a botanical garden is an herb garden planted in the shape of a square. The square measures 6 yards on each side. Visitors can view the herbs from a diagonal pathway through the garden. How long is the pathway?

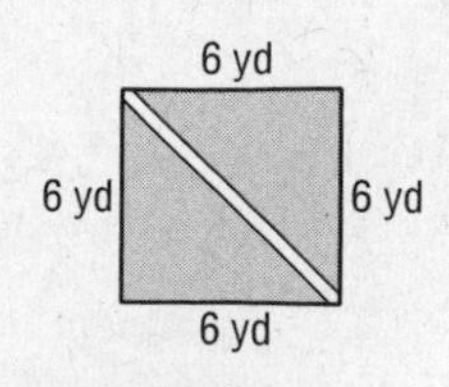

NAME ______________________ DATE __________ PERIOD __________

8-3 Word Problem Practice

Special Right Triangles

1. **ORIGAMI** A square piece of paper 150 millimeters on a side is folded in half along a diagonal. The result is a 45°-45°-90° triangle. What is the length of the hypotenuse of this triangle?

2. **ESCALATORS** A 40-foot-long escalator rises from the first floor to the second floor of a shopping mall. The escalator makes a 30° angle with the horizontal.

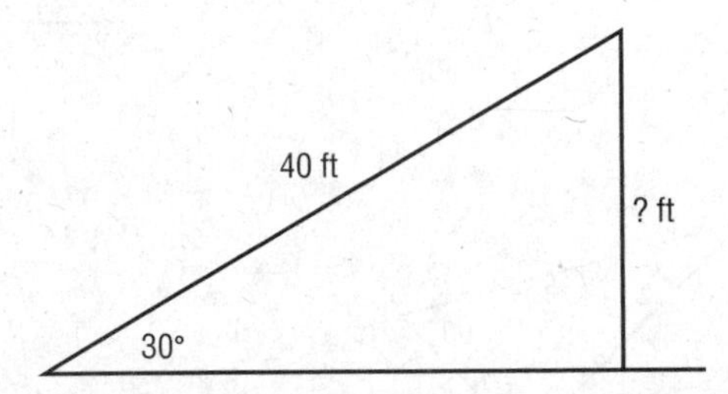

How high above the first floor is the second floor?

3. **HEXAGONS** A box of chocolates shaped like a regular hexagon is placed snugly inside of a rectangular box as shown in the figure.

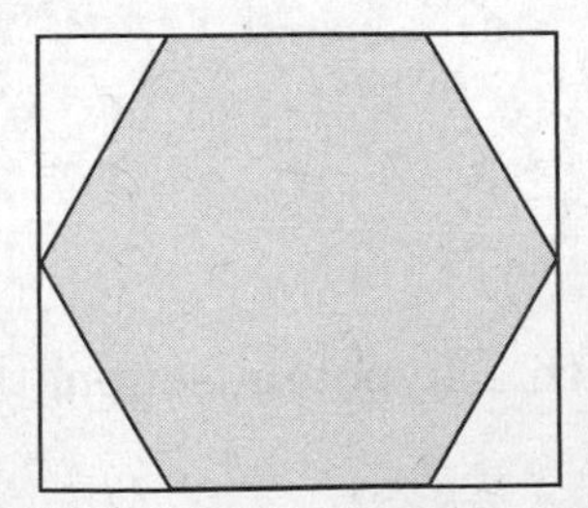

If the side length of the hexagon is 3 inches, what are the dimensions of the rectangular box?

4. **WINDOWS** A large stained glass window is constructed from six 30°-60°-90° triangles as shown in the figure.

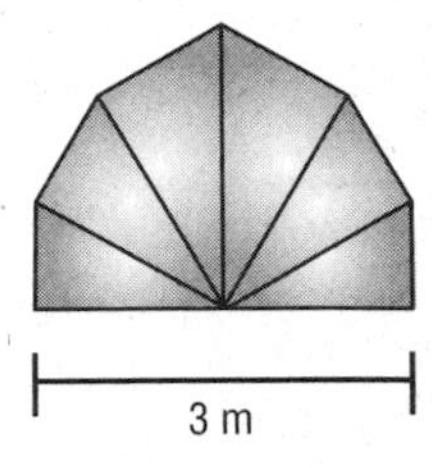

What is the height of the window?

5. **MOVIES** Kim and Yolanda are watching a movie in a movie theater. Yolanda is sitting x feet from the screen and Kim is 15 feet behind Yolanda.

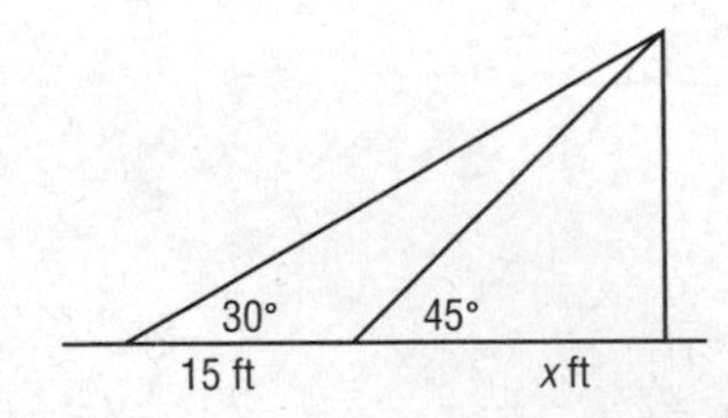

The angle that Kim's line of sight to the top of the screen makes with the horizontal is 30°. The angle that Yolanda's line of sight to the top of the screen makes with the horizontal is 45°.

a. How high is the top of the screen in terms of x?

b. What is $\frac{x + 15}{x}$?

c. How far is Yolanda from the screen? Round your answer to the nearest tenth.

8-3 Enrichment

Constructing Values of Square Roots

The diagram at the right shows a right isosceles triangle with two legs of length 1 inch. By the Pythagorean Theorem, the length of the hypotenuse is $\sqrt{2}$ inches. By constructing an adjacent right triangle with legs of $\sqrt{2}$ inches and 1 inch, you can create a segment of length $\sqrt{3}$.

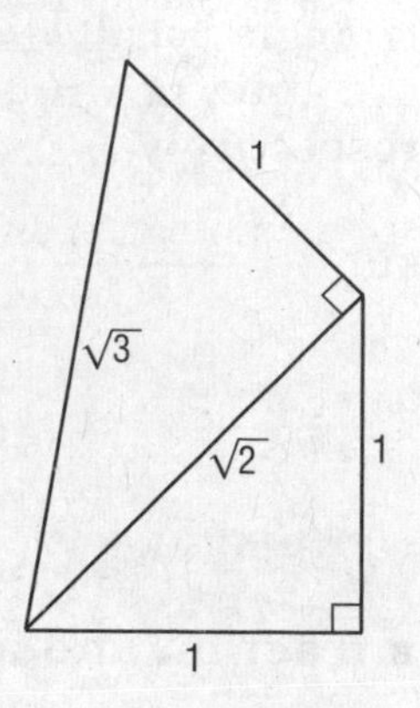

By continuing this process as shown below, you can construct a "wheel" of square roots. This wheel is called the "Wheel of Theodorus" after a Greek philosopher who lived about 400 B.C.

Continue constructing the wheel until you make a segment of length $\sqrt{18}$.

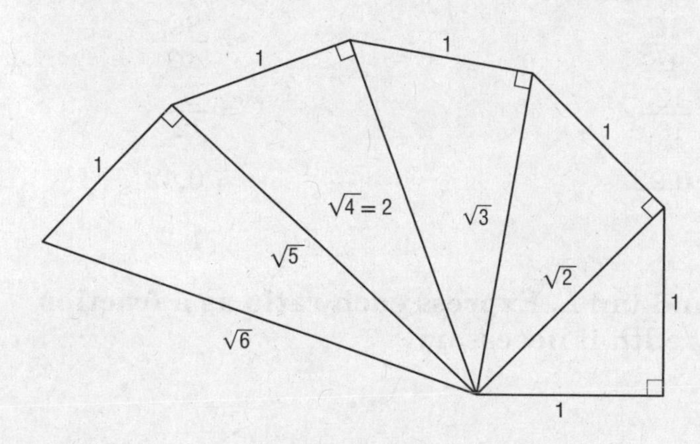

NAME ______________________ DATE __________ PERIOD __________

8-4 Study Guide and Intervention

Trigonometry

Trigonometric Ratios The ratio of the lengths of two sides of a right triangle is called a **trigonometric ratio.** The three most common ratios are **sine, cosine,** and **tangent,** which are abbreviated *sin*, *cos*, and *tan*, respectively.

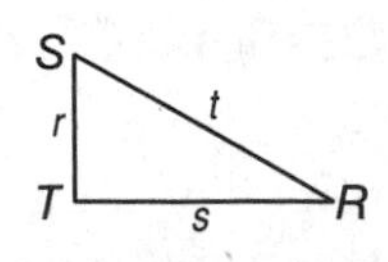

$\sin R = \frac{\text{leg opposite } \angle R}{\text{hypotenuse}} = \frac{r}{t}$

$\cos R = \frac{\text{leg adjacent to } \angle R}{\text{hypotenuse}} = \frac{s}{t}$

$\tan R = \frac{\text{leg opposite } \angle R}{\text{leg adjacent to } \angle R} = \frac{r}{s}$

Example **Find sin *A*, cos *A*, and tan *A*. Express each ratio as a fraction and a decimal to the nearest hundredth.**

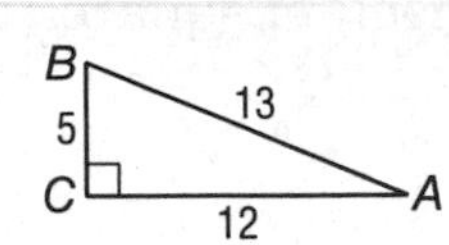

$\sin A = \frac{\text{opposite leg}}{\text{hypotenuse}} = \frac{BC}{BA} = \frac{5}{13} \approx 0.38$

$\cos A = \frac{\text{adjacent leg}}{\text{hypotenuse}} = \frac{AC}{AB} = \frac{12}{13} \approx 0.92$

$\tan A = \frac{\text{opposite leg}}{\text{adjacent leg}} = \frac{BC}{AC} = \frac{5}{12} \approx 0.42$

Exercises

Find sin *J*, cos *J*, tan *J*, sin *L*, cos *L*, and tan *L*. Express each ratio as a fraction and as a decimal to the nearest hundredth if necessary.

1.

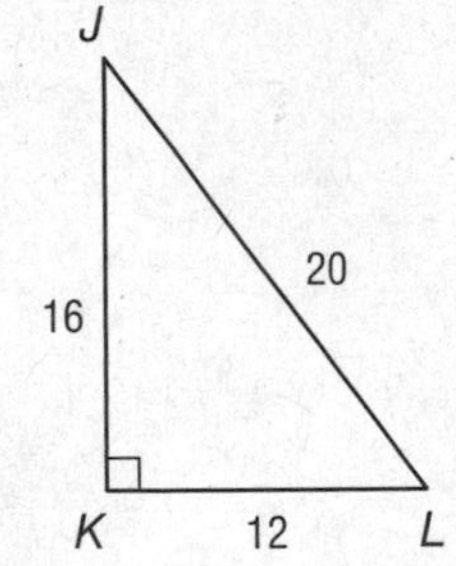

2.

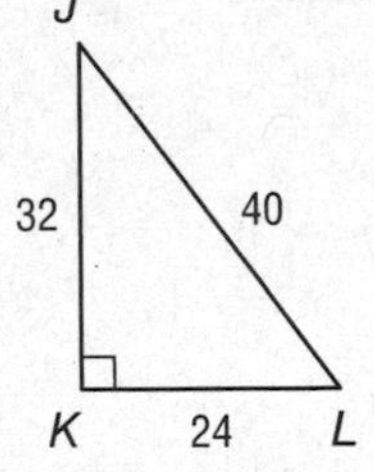

3.

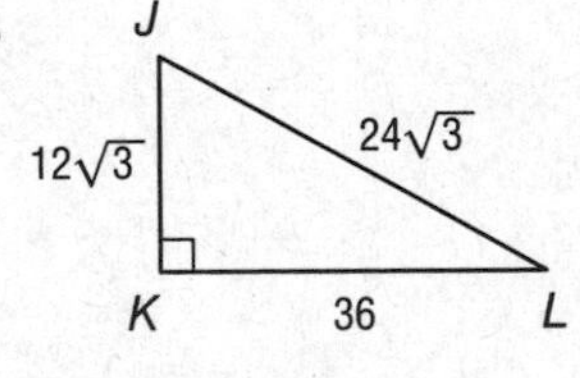

NAME ______________________ DATE ____________ PERIOD ____________

8-4 Study Guide and Intervention *(continued)*

Trigonometry

Use Inverse Trigonometric Ratios You can use a calculator and the sine, cosine, or tangent to find the measure of the angle, called the **inverse** of the trigonometric ratio.

Example **Use a calculator to find the measure of $\angle T$ to the nearest tenth.**

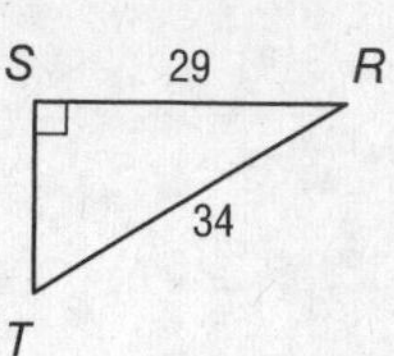

The measures given are those of the leg opposite $\angle T$ and the hypotenuse, so write an equation using the sine ratio.

$\sin T = \frac{opp}{hyp}$ $\quad \sin T = \frac{29}{34}$

If $\sin T = \frac{29}{34}$, then $\sin^{-1} \frac{29}{34} = m\angle T$.

Use a calculator. So, $m\angle T \approx 58.5$.

Exercises

Use a calculator to find the measure of $\angle T$ to the nearest tenth.

1.

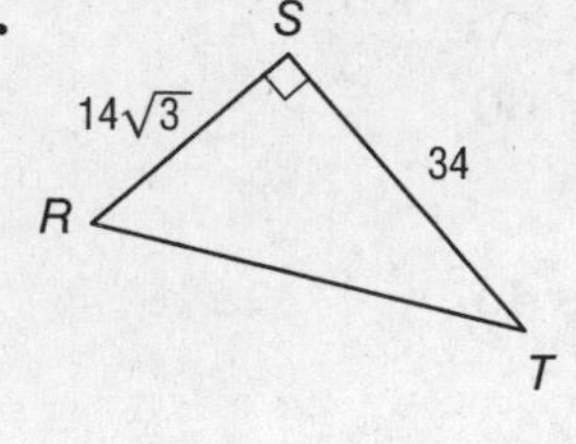

2.

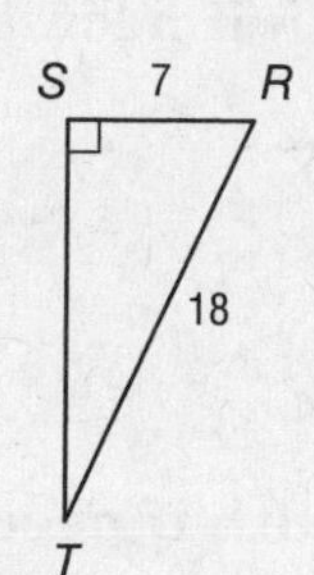

3.

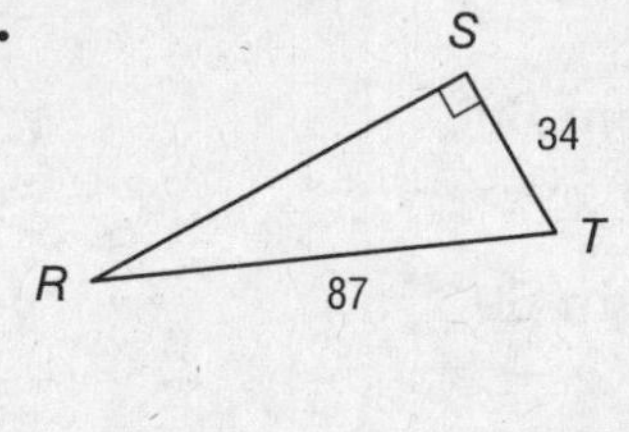

4.

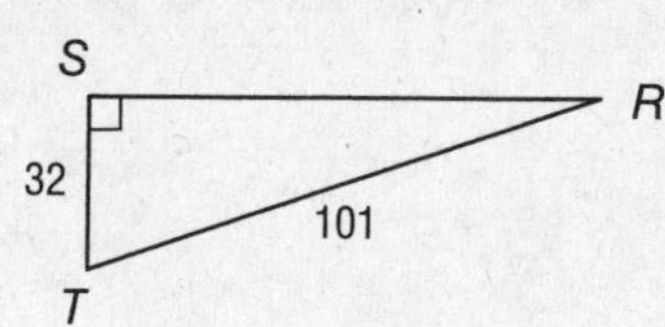

5.

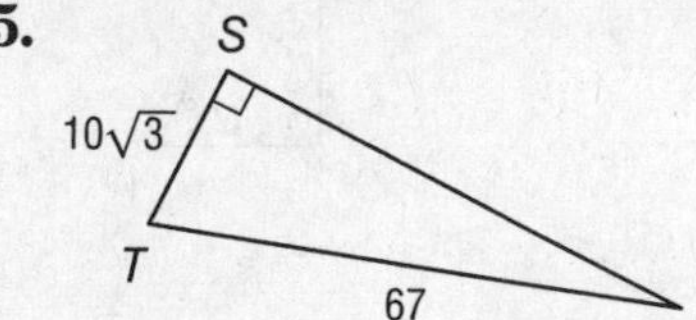

6.

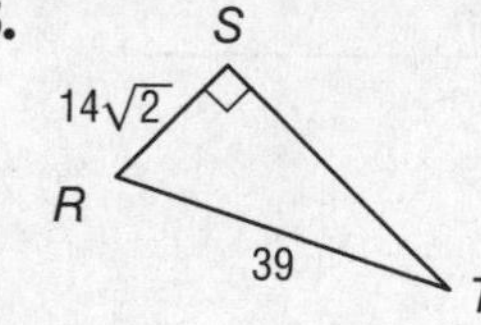

NAME ______________________ DATE ____________ PERIOD ____________

8-4 Skills Practice

Trigonometry

Find sin R, cos R, tan R, sin S, cos S, and tan S. Express each ratio as a fraction and as a decimal to the nearest hundredth.

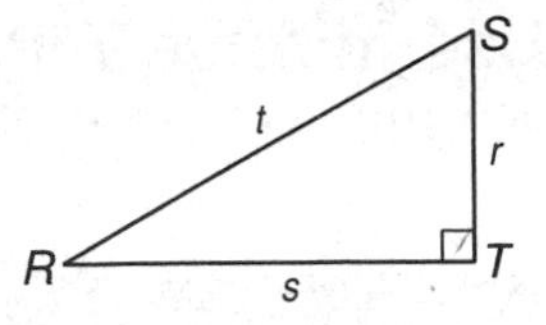

1. $r = 16$, $s = 30$, $t = 34$

2. $r = 10$, $s = 24$, $t = 26$

Use a special right triangle to express each trigonometric ratio as a fraction and as a decimal to the nearest hundredth if necessary.

3. sin 30°

4. tan 45°

5. cos 60°

6. sin 60°

7. tan 30°

8. cos 45°

Find x. Round to the nearest hundredth if necessary.

9.

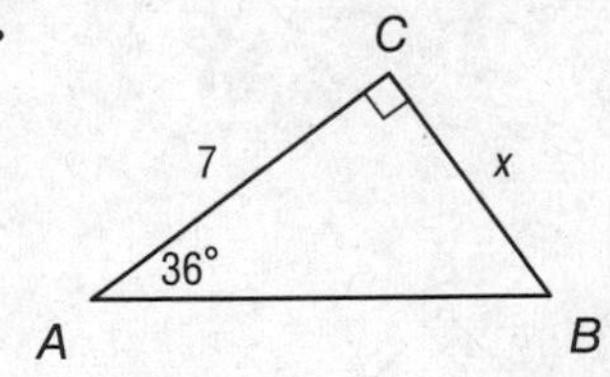

10.

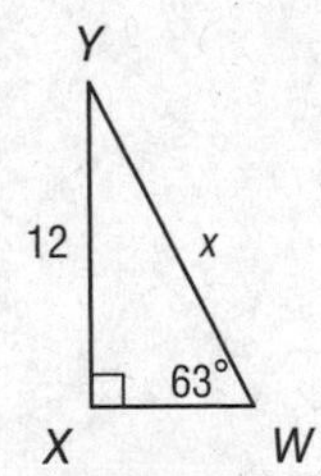

11.

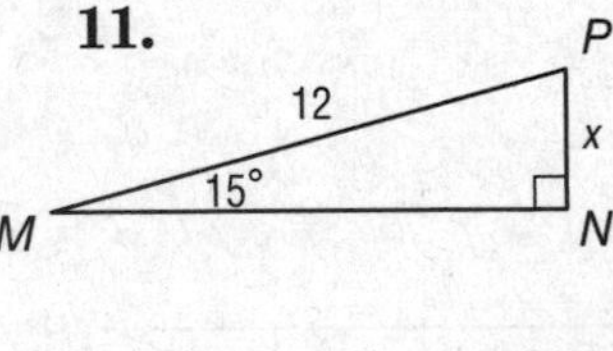

Use a calculator to find the measure of $\angle B$ to the nearest tenth.

12.

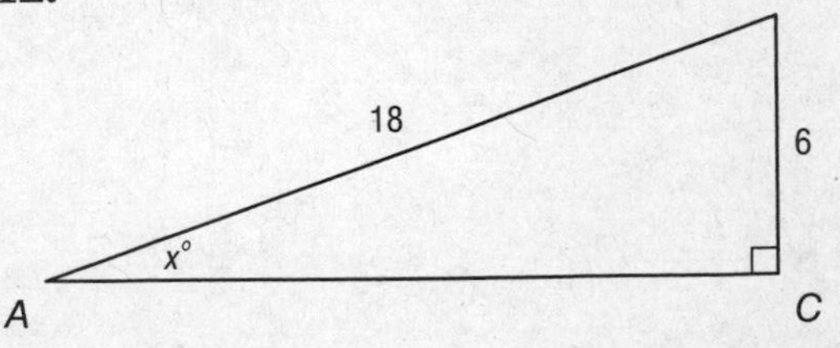

13.

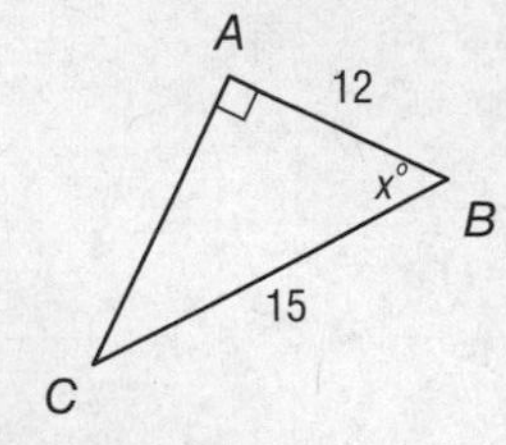

14.

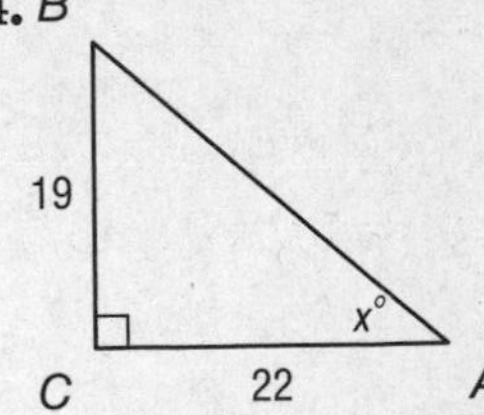

NAME ______________________ DATE __________ PERIOD __________

8-4 Practice

Trigonometry

Find sin *L*, cos *L*, tan *L*, sin *M*, cos *M*, and tan *M*. Express each ratio as a fraction and as a decimal to the nearest hundredth.

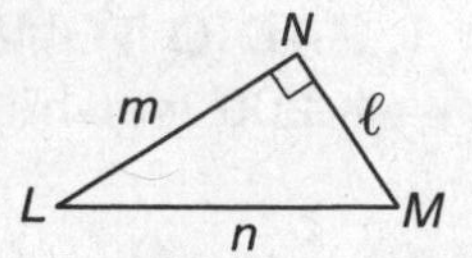

1. $\ell = 15, m = 36, n = 39$

2. $\ell = 12, m = 12\sqrt{3}, n = 24$

Find *x*. Round to the nearest hundredth.

3.

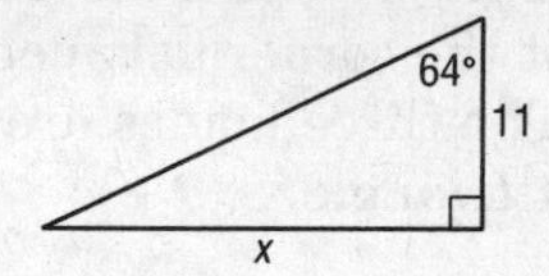

4.

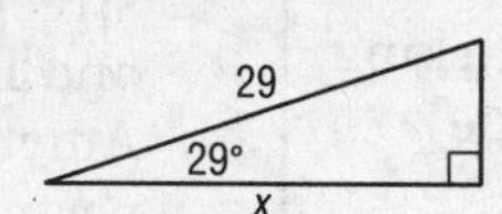

5.

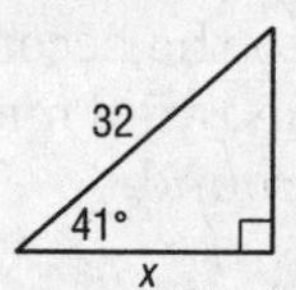

Use a calculator to find the measure of ∠*B* to the nearest tenth.

6.

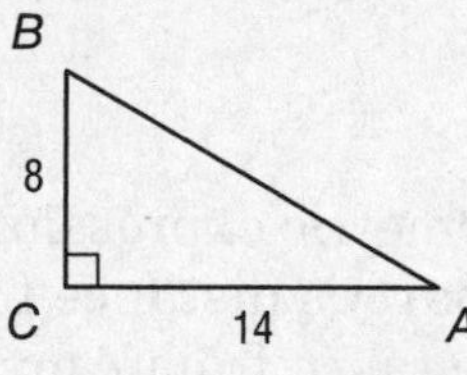

7.

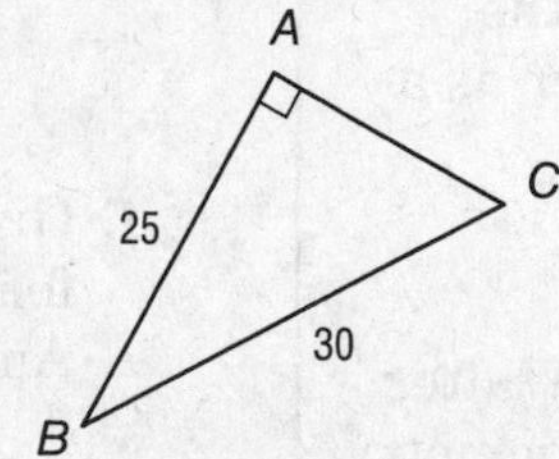

8.

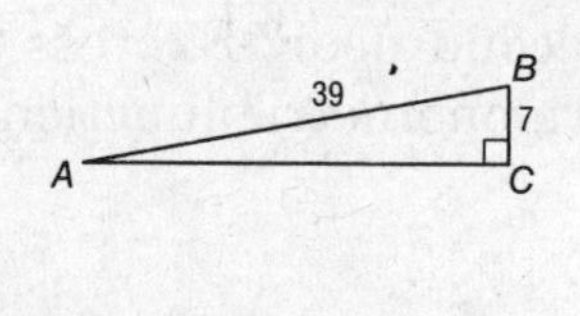

9. GEOGRAPHY Diego used a theodolite to map a region of land for his class in geomorphology. To determine the elevation of a vertical rock formation, he measured the distance from the base of the formation to his position and the angle between the ground and the line of sight to the top of the formation. The distance was 43 meters and the angle was 36°. What is the height of the formation to the nearest meter?

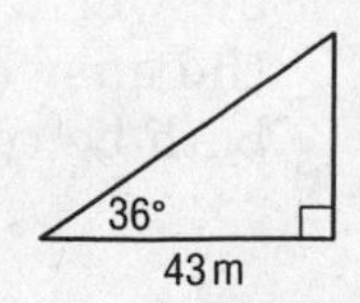

NAME ______________________ DATE ____________ PERIOD ____________

8-4 Word Problem Practice

Trigonometry

1. RADIO TOWERS Kay is standing near a 200-foot-high radio tower.

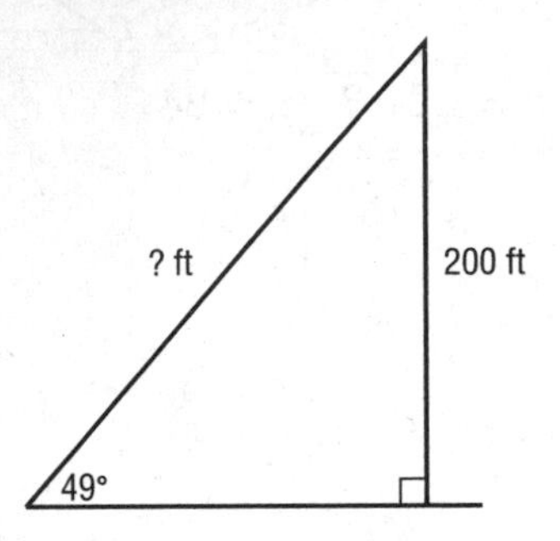

Use the information in the figure to determine how far Kay is from the top of the tower. Express your answer as a trigonometric function.

2. RAMPS A 60-foot ramp rises from the first floor to the second floor of a parking garage. The ramp makes a 15° angle with the ground.

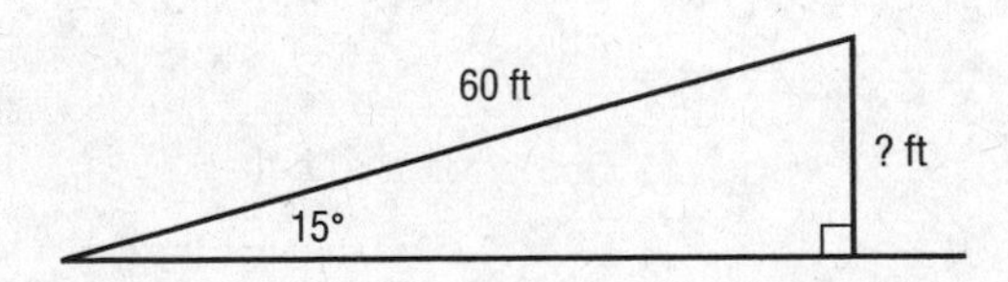

How high above the first floor is the second floor? Express your answer as a trigonometric function.

3. TRIGONOMETRY Melinda and Walter were both solving the same trigonometry problem. However, after they finished their computations, Melinda said the answer was 52 sin 27° and Walter said the answer was 52 cos 63°. Could they both be correct? Explain.

4. LINES Jasmine draws line m on a coordinate plane.

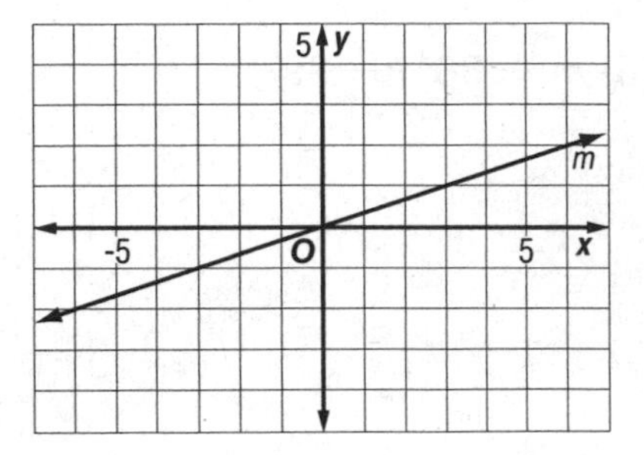

What angle does m make with the x-axis? Round your answer to the nearest degree.

5. NEIGHBORS Amy, Barry, and Chris live on the same block. Chris lives up the street and around the corner from Amy, and Barry lives at the corner between Amy and Chris. The three homes are the vertices of a right triangle.

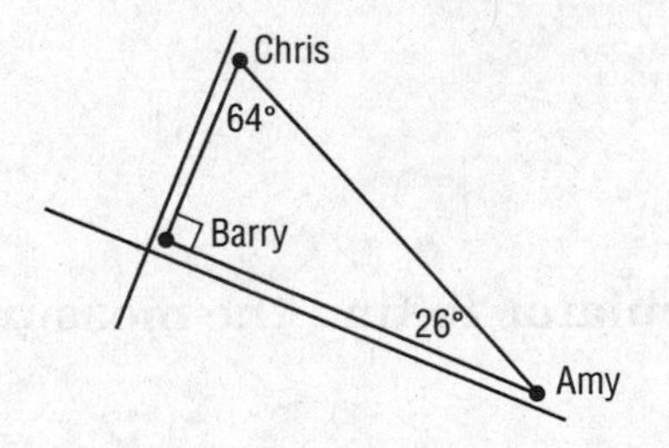

a. Give two trigonometric expressions for the ratio of Barry's distance from Amy to Chris' distance from Amy.

b. Give two trigonometric expressions for the ratio of Barry's distance from Chris to Amy's distance from Chris.

c. Give a trigonometric expression for the ratio of Amy's distance from Barry to Chris' distance from Barry.

NAME ______________________ DATE __________ PERIOD __________

8-4 Enrichment

Sine and Cosine of Angles

The following diagram can be used to obtain approximate values for the sine and cosine of angles from 0° to 90°. The radius of the circle is 1. So, the sine and cosine values can be read directly from the vertical and horizontal axes.

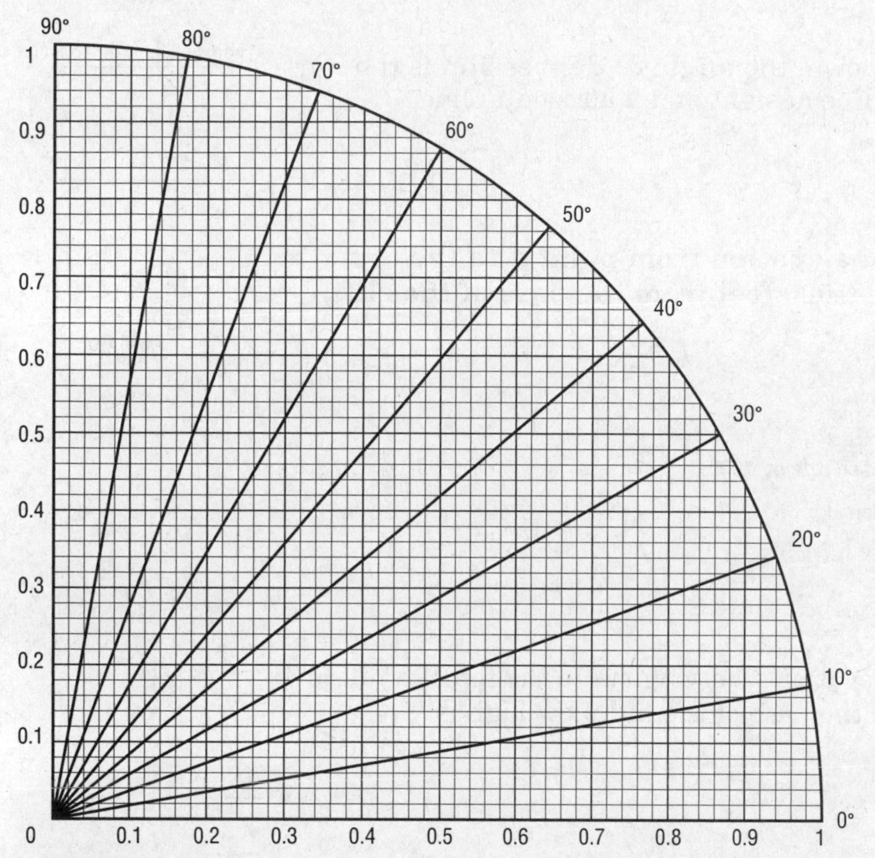

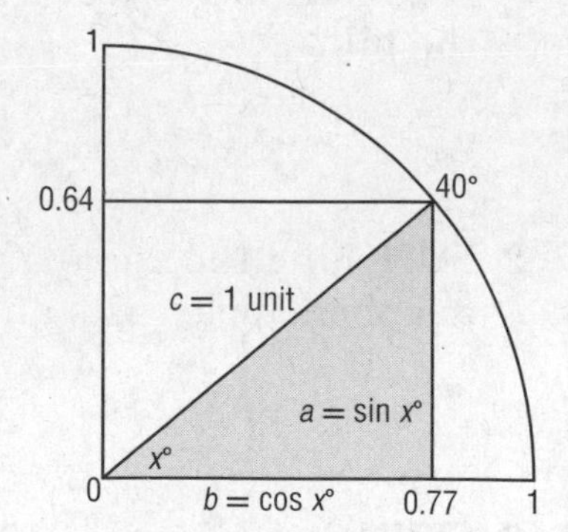

Example **Find approximate values for sin 40° and cos 40°. Consider the triangle formed by the segment marked 40°, as illustrated by the shaded triangle at right.**

$\sin 40° = \frac{a}{c} \approx \frac{0.64}{1}$ or 0.64 $\qquad \cos 40° = \frac{b}{c} \approx \frac{0.77}{1}$ or 0.77

1. Use the diagram above to complete the chart of values.

$x°$	0°	10°	20°	30°	40°	50°	60°	70°	80°	90°
sin $x°$					0.64					
cos $x°$					0.77					

2. Compare the sine and cosine of two complementary angles (angles with a sum of 90°). What do you notice?

Lesson 8-4

NAME ______________________ DATE ____________ PERIOD ____________

8-5 Study Guide and Intervention

Angles of Elevation and Depression

Angles of Elevation and Depression Many real-world problems that involve looking up to an object can be described in terms of an **angle of elevation,** which is the angle between an observer's line of sight and a horizontal line.

When an observer is looking down, the **angle of depression** is the angle between the observer's line of sight and a horizontal line.

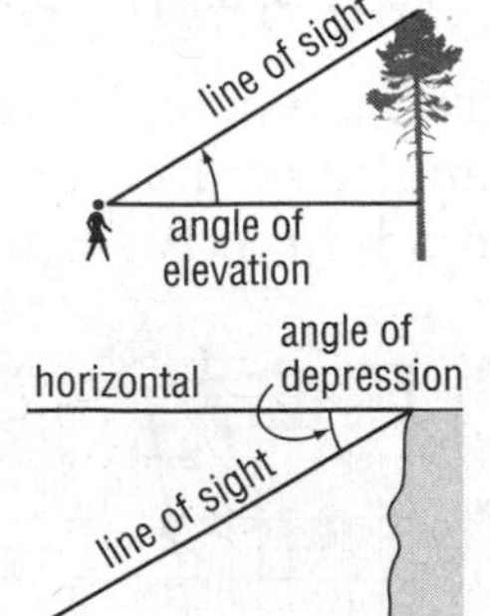

Example **The angle of elevation from point A to the top of a cliff is 34°. If point A is 1000 feet from the base of the cliff, how high is the cliff?**

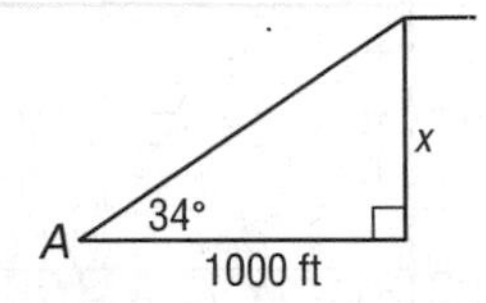

Let x = the height of the cliff.

$\tan 34° = \frac{x}{1000}$ $\quad$ $\tan = \frac{\text{opposite}}{\text{adjacent}}$

$1000(\tan 34°) = x$ $\quad$ Multiply each side by 1000.

$674.5 \approx x$ $\quad$ Use a calculator.

The height of the cliff is about 674.5 feet.

Exercises

1. **HILL TOP** The angle of elevation from point A to the top of a hill is 49°. If point A is 400 feet from the base of the hill, how high is the hill?

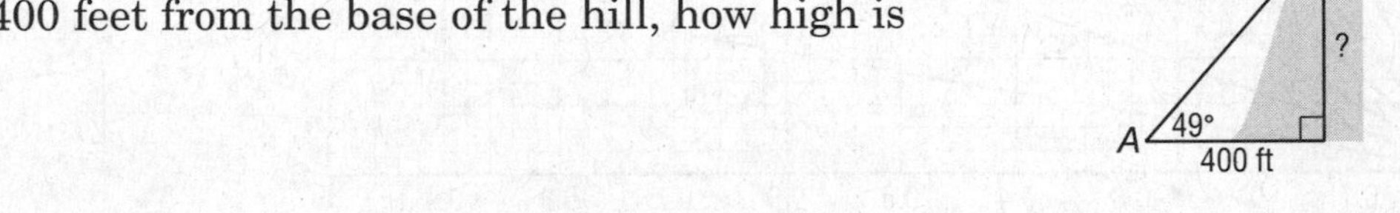

2. **SUN** Find the angle of elevation of the Sun when a 12.5-meter-tall telephone pole casts an 18-meter-long shadow.

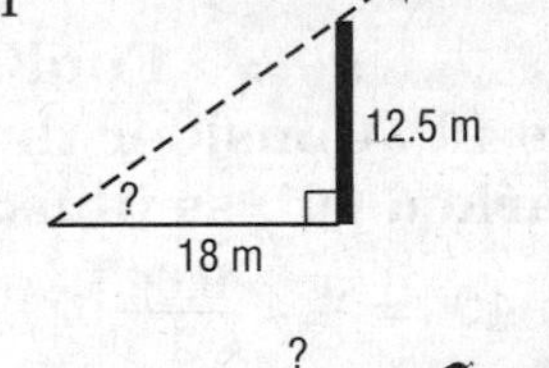

3. **SKIING** A ski run is 1000 yards long with a vertical drop of 208 yards. Find the angle of depression from the top of the ski run to the bottom.

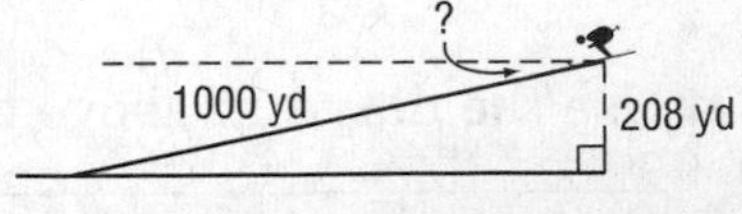

4. **AIR TRAFFIC** From the top of a 120-foot-high tower, an air traffic controller observes an airplane on the runway at an angle of depression of 19°. How far from the base of the tower is the airplane?

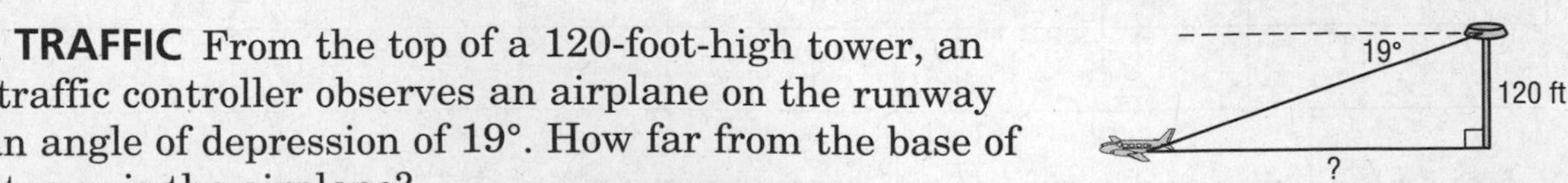

8-5 Study Guide and Intervention *(continued)*

Angles of Elevation and Depression

Two Angles of Elevation or Depression Angles of elevation or depression to two different objects can be used to estimate distance between those objects. The angles from two different positions of observation to the same object can be used to estimate the height of the object.

Example **To estimate the height of a garage, Jason sights the top of the garage at a 42° angle of elevation. He then steps back 20 feet and sites the top at a 10° angle. If Jason is 6 feet tall, how tall is the garage to the nearest foot?**

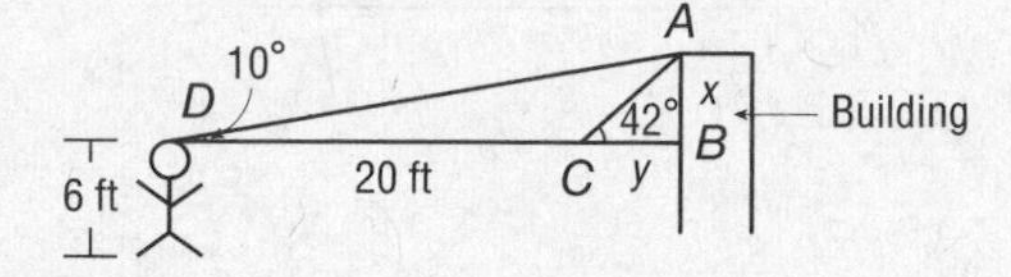

$\triangle ABC$ and $\triangle ABD$ are right triangles. We can determine $AB = x$ and $CB = y$, and $DB = y + 20$.

Use $\triangle ABC$.

$\tan 42° = \frac{x}{y}$ or $y \tan 42° = x$

Use $\triangle ABD$.

$\tan 10° = \frac{x}{y + 20}$ or $(y + 20) \tan 10° = x$

Substitute the value for x from $\triangle ABD$ in the equation for $\triangle ABC$ and solve for y.

$$y \tan 42° = (y + 20) \tan 10°$$
$$y \tan 42° = y \tan 10° + 20 \tan 10°$$
$$y \tan 42° - y \tan 10° = 20 \tan 10°$$
$$y (\tan 42° - \tan 10°) = 20 \tan 10°$$
$$y = \frac{20 \tan 10°}{\tan 42° - \tan 10°} \approx 4.87$$

If $y \approx 4.87$, then $x = 4.87 \tan 42°$ or about 4.4 feet. Add Jason's height, so the garage is about 4.4 + 6 or 10.4 feet tall.

Exercises

1. CLIFF Sarah stands on the ground and sights the top of a steep cliff at a 60° angle of elevation. She then steps back 50 meters and sights the top of the steep cliff at a 30° angle. If Sarah is 1.8 meters tall, how tall is the steep cliff to the nearest meter?

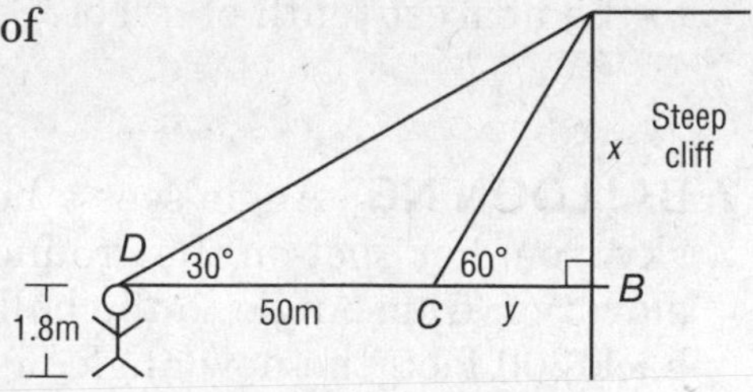

2. BALLOON The angle of depression from a hot air balloon in the air to a person on the ground is 36°. If the person steps back 10 feet, the new angle of depression is 25°. If the person is 6 feet tall, how far off the ground is the hot air balloon?

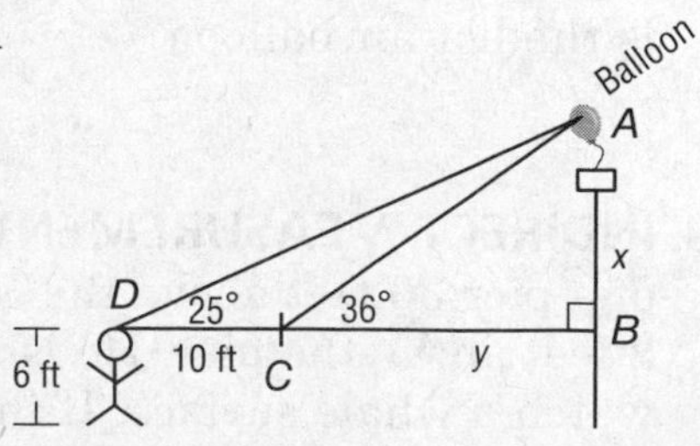

NAME ______________________ DATE ____________ PERIOD ____________

8-5 Skills Practice

Angles of Elevation and Depression

Name the angle of depression or angle of elevation in each figure.

1.

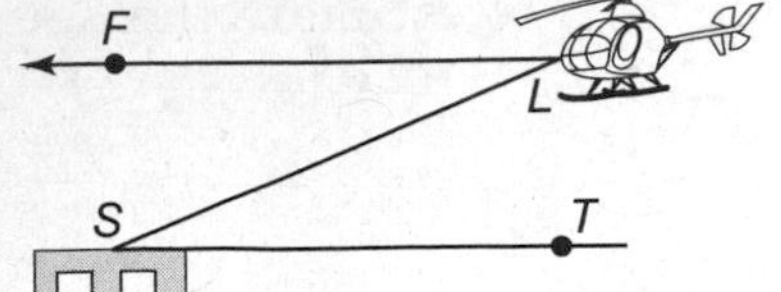

2.

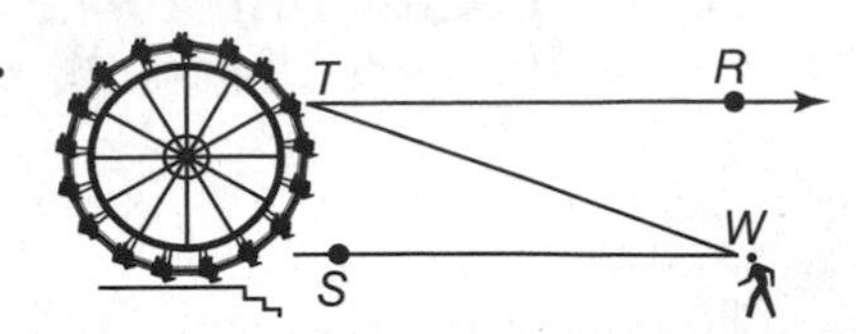

3.

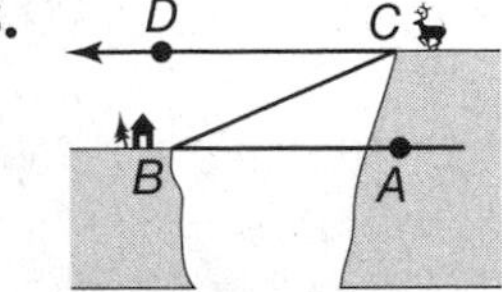

4.

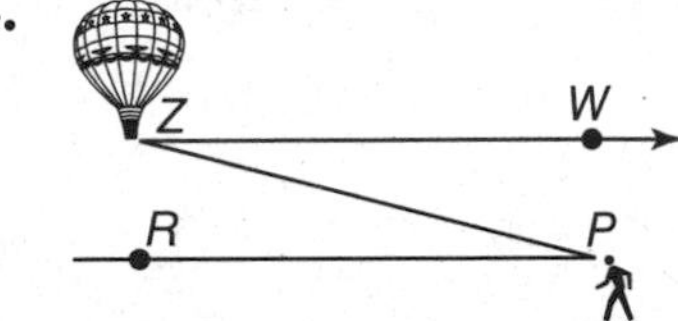

5. **MOUNTAIN BIKING** On a mountain bike trip along the Gemini Bridges Trail in Moab, Utah, Nabuko stopped on the canyon floor to get a good view of the twin sandstone bridges. Nabuko is standing about 60 meters from the base of the canyon cliff, and the natural arch bridges are about 100 meters up the canyon wall. If her line of sight is 5 metres above the ground, what is the angle of elevation to the top of the bridges? Round to the nearest tenth degree.

6. **SHADOWS** Suppose the sun casts a shadow off a 35-foot building. If the angle of elevation to the sun is 60°, how long is the shadow to the nearest tenth of a foot?

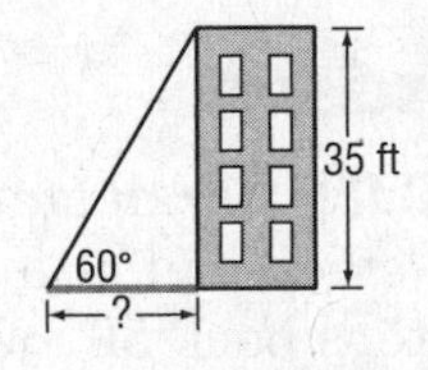

7. **BALLOONING** Angie sees a hot air balloon in the sky from her spot on the ground. The angle of elevation from Angie to the balloon is 40°. If she steps back 200 feet, the new angle of elevation is 10°. If Angie is 5.5 feet tall, how far off the ground is the hot air balloon?

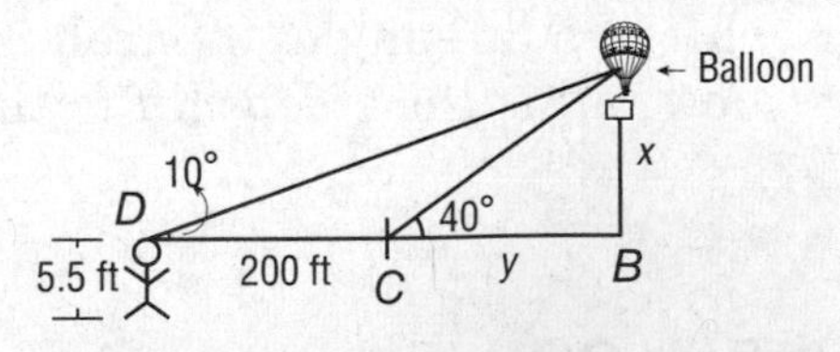

8. **INDIRECT MEASUREMENT** Kyle is at the end of a pier 30 feet above the ocean. His eye level is 3 feet above the pier. He is using binoculars to watch a whale surface. If the angle of depression of the whale is 20°, how far is the whale from Kyle's binoculars? Round to the nearest tenth foot.

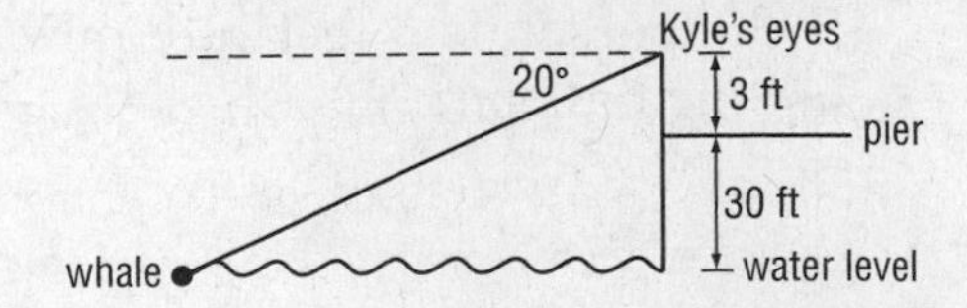

NAME ______________________ DATE __________ PERIOD __________

8-5 Practice

Angles of Elevation and Depression

Name the angle of depression or angle of elevation in each figure.

1. 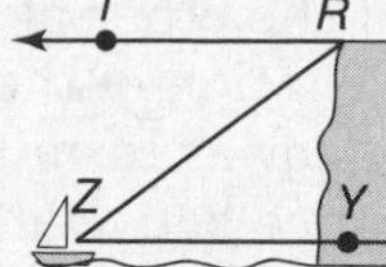

2. 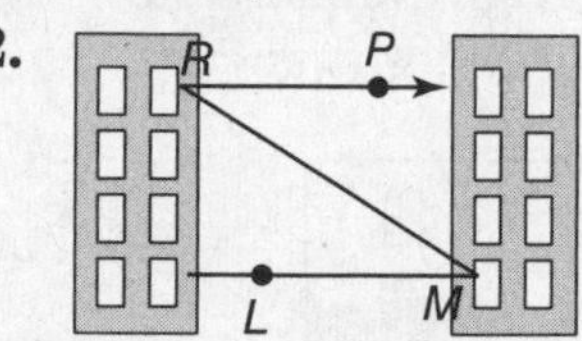

3. **WATER TOWERS** A student can see a water tower from the closest point of the soccer field at San Lobos High School. The edge of the soccer field is about 110 feet from the water tower and the water tower stands at a height of 32.5 feet. What is the angle of elevation if the eye level of the student viewing the tower from the edge of the soccer field is 6 feet above the ground? Round to the nearest tenth.

4. **CONSTRUCTION** A roofer props a ladder against a wall so that the top of the ladder reaches a 30-foot roof that needs repair. If the angle of elevation from the bottom of the ladder to the roof is 55°, how far is the ladder from the base of the wall? Round your answer to the nearest foot.

5. **TOWN ORDINANCES** The town of Belmont restricts the height of flagpoles to 25 feet on any property. Lindsay wants to determine whether her school is in compliance with the regulation. Her eye level is 5.5 feet from the ground and she stands 36 feet from the flagpole. If the angle of elevation is about 25°, what is the height of the flagpole to the nearest tenth?

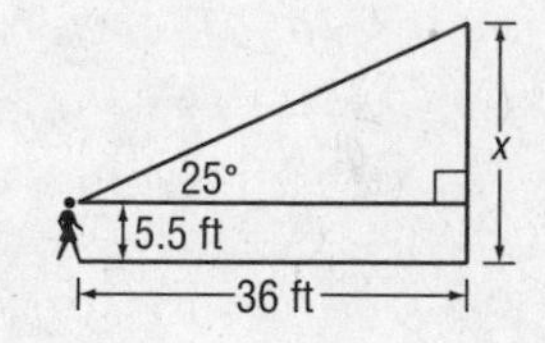

6. **GEOGRAPHY** Stephan is standing on the ground by a mesa in the Painted Desert. Stephan is 1.8 meters tall and sights the top of the mesa at 29°. Stephan steps back 100 meters and sights the top at 25°. How tall is the mesa?

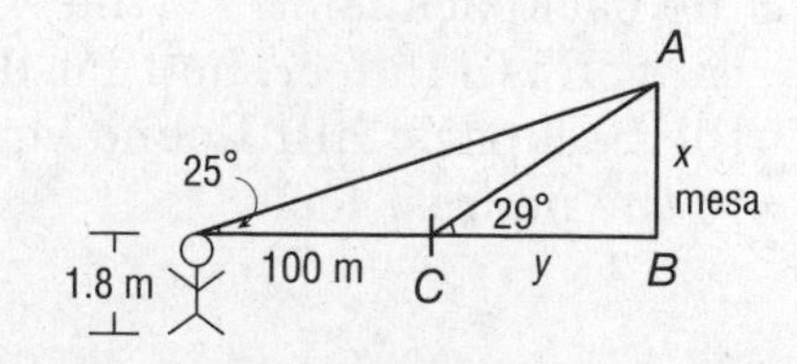

7. **INDIRECT MEASUREMENT** Mr. Dominguez is standing on a 40-foot ocean bluff near his home. He can see his two dogs on the beach below. If his line of sight is 6 feet above the ground and the angles of depression to his dogs are 34° and 48°, how far apart are the dogs to the nearest foot?

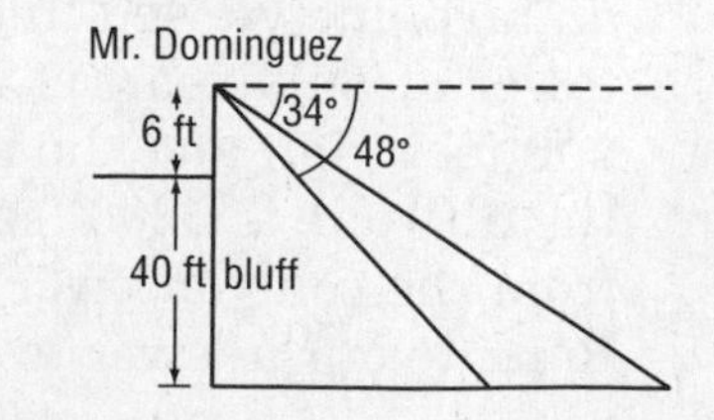

Lesson 8-5

NAME ______________________ DATE ____________ PERIOD ____________

8-5 Word Problem Practice

Angles of Elevation and Depression

1. LIGHTHOUSES Sailors on a ship at sea spot the light from a lighthouse. The angle of elevation to the light is 25°.

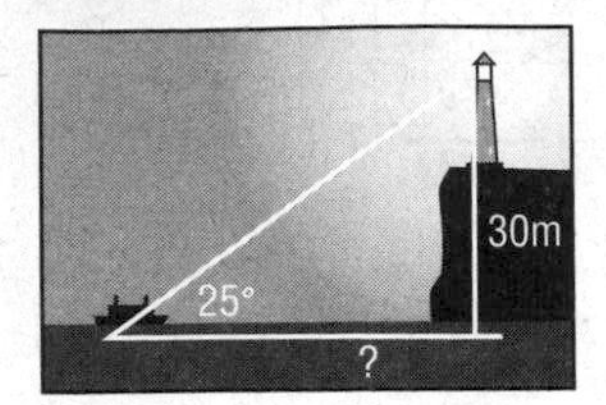

The light of the lighthouse is 30 meters above sea level. How far from the shore is the ship? Round your answer to the nearest meter.

2. RESCUE A hiker dropped his backpack over one side of a canyon onto a ledge below. Because of the shape of the cliff, he could not see exactly where it landed.

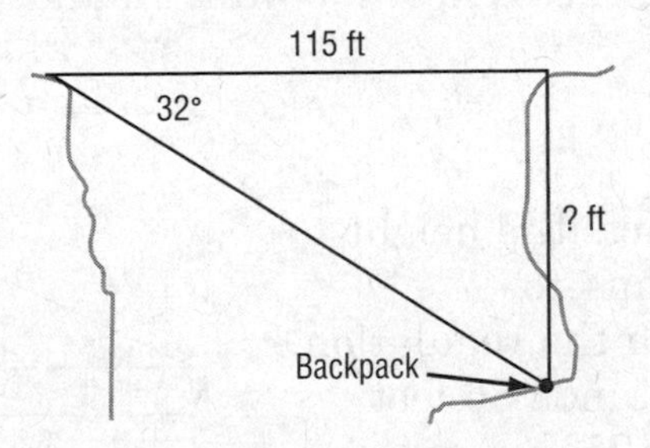

From the other side, the park ranger reports that the angle of depression to the backpack is 32°. If the width of the canyon is 115 feet, how far down did the backpack fall? Round your answer to the nearest foot.

3. AIRPLANES The angle of elevation to an airplane viewed from the control tower at an airport is 7°. The tower is 200 feet high and the pilot reports that the altitude is 5200 feet. How far away from the control tower is the airplane? Round your answer to the nearest foot.

4. PEAK TRAM The Peak Tram in Hong Kong connects two terminals, one at the base of a mountain, and the other at the summit. The angle of elevation of the upper terminal from the lower terminal is about 15.5°. The distance between the two terminals is about 1365 meters. About how much higher above sea level is the upper terminal compared to the lower terminal? Round your answer to the nearest meter.

5. HELICOPTERS Jermaine and John are watching a helicopter hover above the ground.

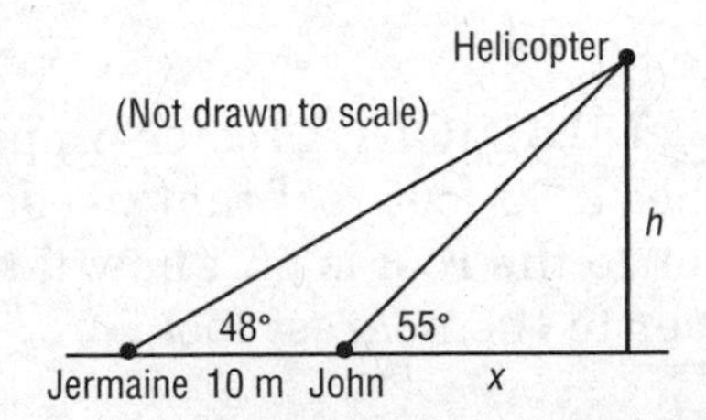

Jermaine and John are standing 10 meters apart.

a. Find two different expressions that can be used to find the h, height of the helicopter.

b. Equate the two expressions you found for Exercise a to solve for x. Round your answer to the nearest hundredth.

c. How high above the ground is the helicopter? Round your answer to the nearest hundredth.

NAME ______________________________ DATE ____________ PERIOD ____________

8-5 Enrichment

Best Seat in the House

Most people want to sit in the best seat in the movie theater. The best seat could be defined as the seat that allows you to see the maximum amount of screen. The picture below represents this situation.

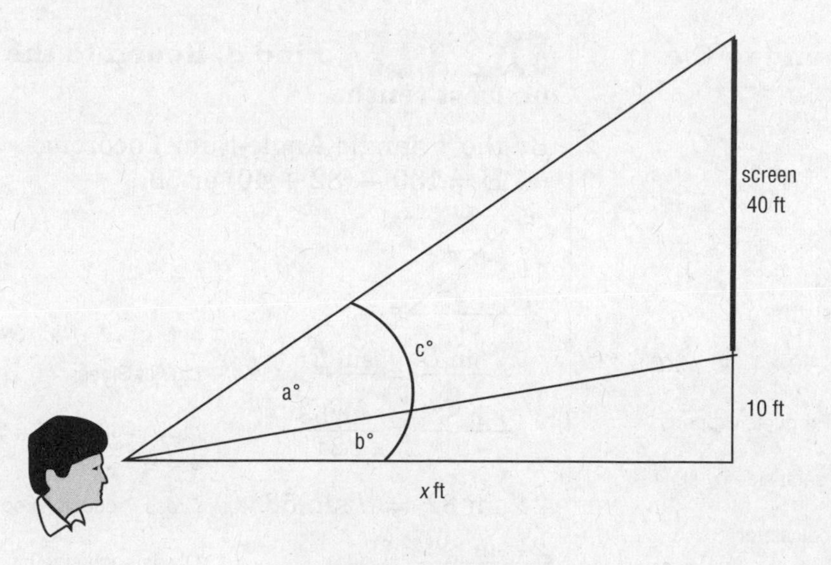

To determine the best seat in the house, you want to find what value of x allows you to see the maximum amount of screen. The value of x is how far from the screen you should sit.

1. To maximize the amount of screen viewed, which angle value needs to be maximized? Why?

2. What is the value of a if $x = 10$ feet?

3. What is the value of a if $x = 20$ feet?

4. What is the value of a if $x = 25$ feet?

5. What is the value of a if $x = 35$ feet?

6. What is the value of a if $x = 55$ feet?

7. Which value of x gives the greatest value of a? So, where is the best seat in the movie theater?

NAME ______________________ DATE __________ PERIOD __________

8-6 Study Guide and Intervention

The Law of Sines and Law of Cosines

The Law of Sines In any triangle, there is a special relationship between the angles of the triangle and the lengths of the sides opposite the angles.

Law of Sines	$\frac{\sin A}{a} = \frac{\sin B}{b} = \frac{\sin C}{c}$

Example 1 **Find b. Round to the nearest tenth.**

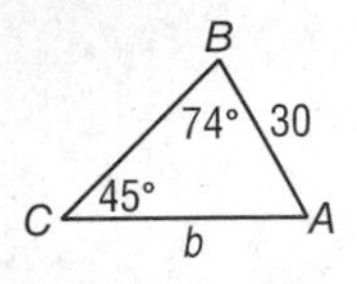

$\frac{\sin C}{c} = \frac{\sin B}{b}$ Law of Sines

$\frac{\sin 45°}{30} = \frac{\sin 74°}{b}$ $m\angle C = 45$, $c = 30$, $m\angle B = 74$

$b \sin 45° = 30 \sin 74°$ Cross Products Property

$b = \frac{30 \sin 74°}{\sin 45°}$ Divide each side by sin 45°.

$b \approx 40.8$ Use a calculator.

Example 2 **Find d. Round to the nearest tenth.**

By the Triangle Angle-Sum Theorem, $m\angle E = 180 - (82 + 40)$ or 58.

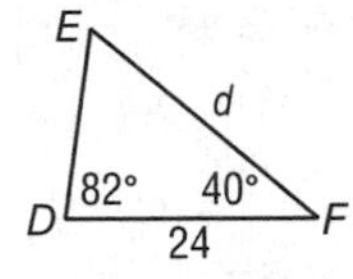

$\frac{\sin D}{d} = \frac{\sin E}{e}$ Law of Sines

$\frac{\sin 82°}{d} = \frac{\sin 58°}{24}$ $m\angle D = 82$, $m\angle E = 58$, $e = 24$

$24 \sin 82° = d \sin 58°$ Cross Products Property

$\frac{24 \sin 82°}{\sin 58°} = d$ Divide each side by sin 58°.

$d \approx 28.0$ Use a calculator.

Exercises

Find x. Round to the nearest tenth.

1.

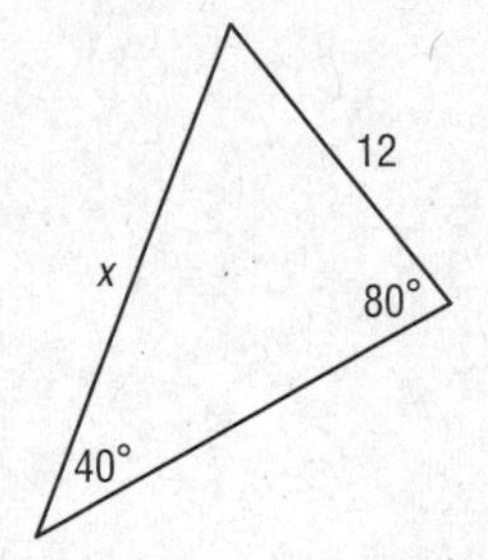

2.

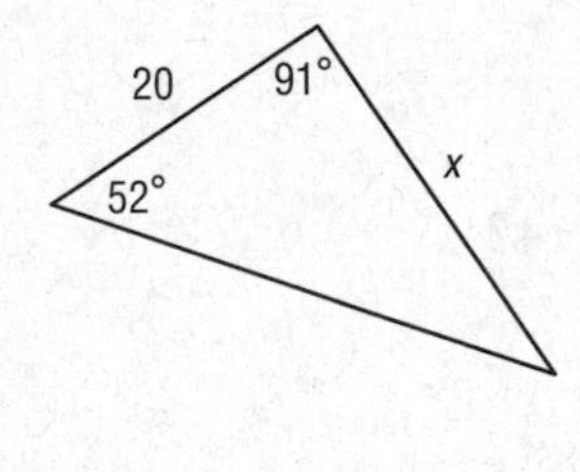

3.

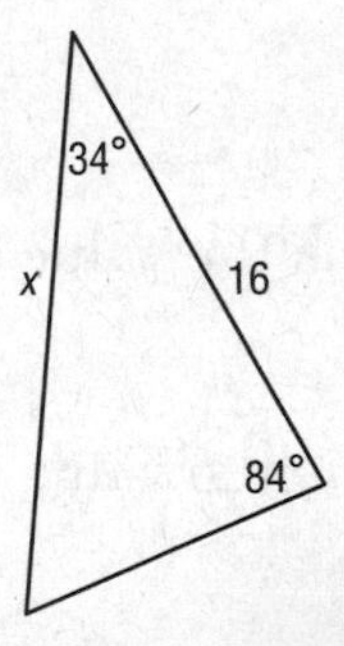

4.

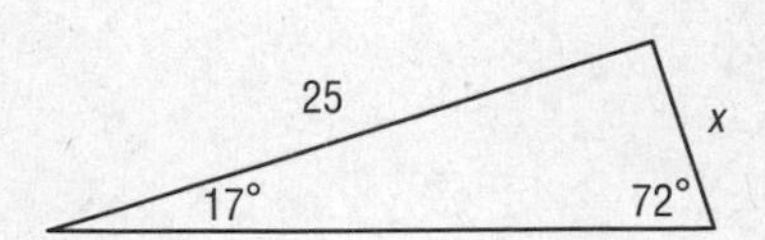

5.

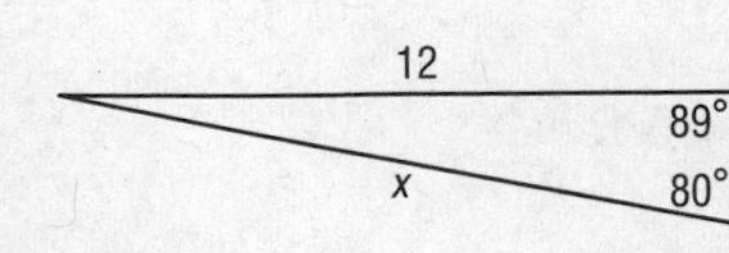

6.

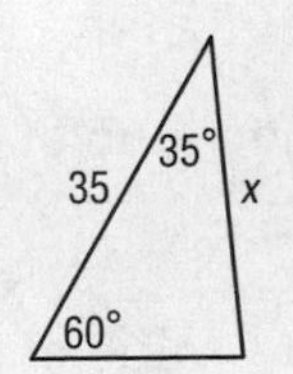

NAME ______________________ DATE __________ PERIOD __________

8-6 Study Guide and Intervention *(continued)*

The Law of Sines and Law of Cosines

Lesson 8-6

The Law of Cosines Another relationship between the sides and angles of any triangle is called the **Law of Cosines.** You can use the Law of Cosines if you know three sides of a triangle or if you know two sides and the included angle of a triangle.

Law of Cosines	Let $\triangle ABC$ be any triangle with a, b, and c representing the measures of the sides opposite the angles with measures A, B, and C, respectively. Then the following equations are true. $a^2 = b^2 + c^2 - 2bc \cos A$ $b^2 = a^2 + c^2 - 2ac \cos B$ $c^2 = a^2 + b^2 - 2ab \cos C$

Example 1 **Find c. Round to the nearest tenth.**

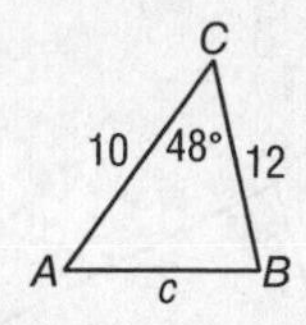

$c^2 = a^2 + b^2 - 2ab \cos C$ — Law of Cosines

$c^2 = 12^2 + 10^2 - 2(12)(10)\cos 48°$ — $a = 12$, $b = 10$, $m\angle C = 48$

$c = \sqrt{12^2 + 10^2 - 2(12)(10)\cos 48°}$ — Take the square root of each side.

$c \approx 9.1$ — Use a calculator.

Example 2 **Find $m\angle A$. Round to the nearest degree.**

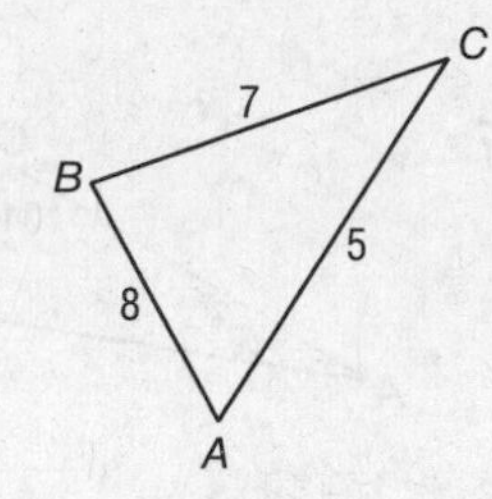

$a^2 = b^2 + c^2 - 2bc \cos A$ — Law of Cosines

$7^2 = 5^2 + 8^2 - 2(5)(8) \cos A$ — $a = 7$, $b = 5$, $c = 8$

$49 = 25 + 64 - 80 \cos A$ — Multiply.

$-40 = -80 \cos A$ — Subtract 89 from each side.

$\frac{1}{2} = \cos A$ — Divide each side by –80.

$\cos^{-1} \frac{1}{2} = A$ — Use the inverse cosine.

$60° = A$ — Use a calculator.

Exercises

Find x. Round angle measures to the nearest degree and side measures to the nearest tenth.

1.

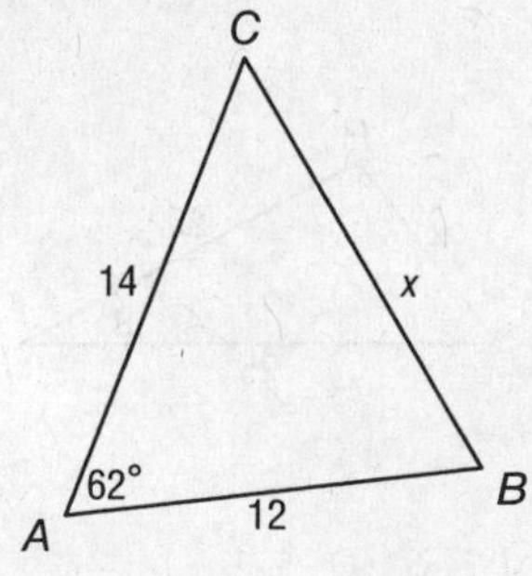

2.

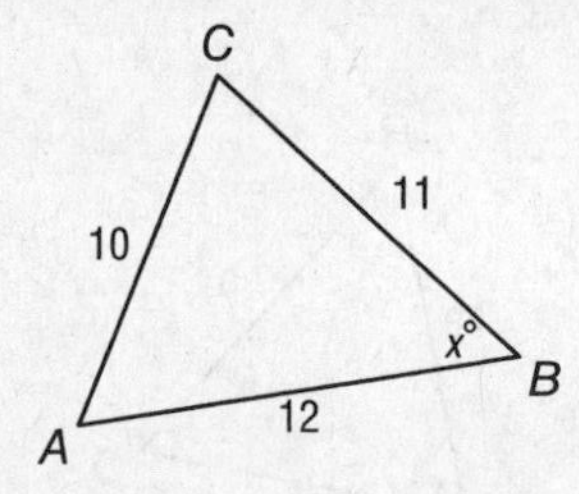

3.

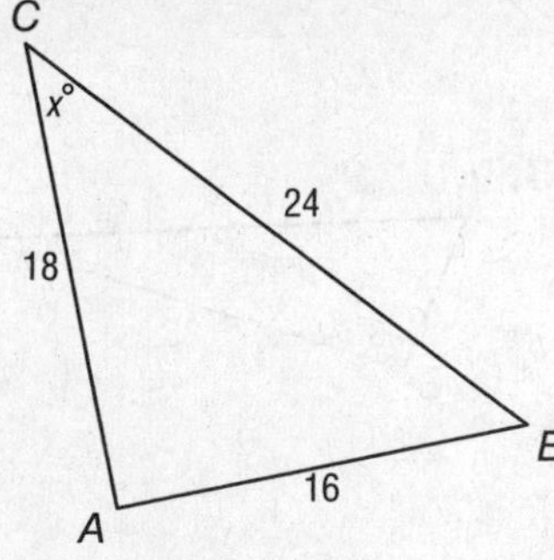

4.

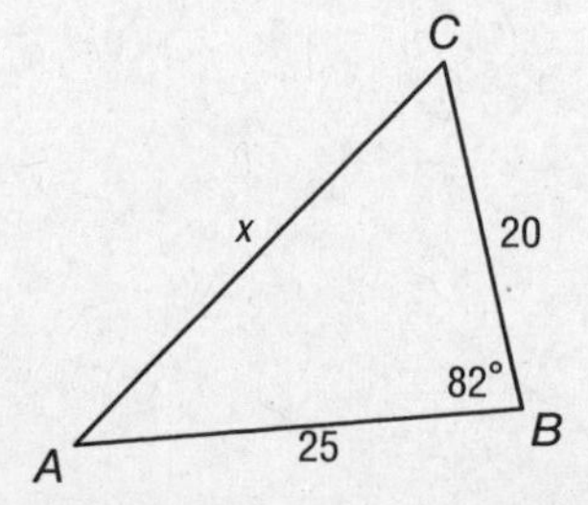

5.

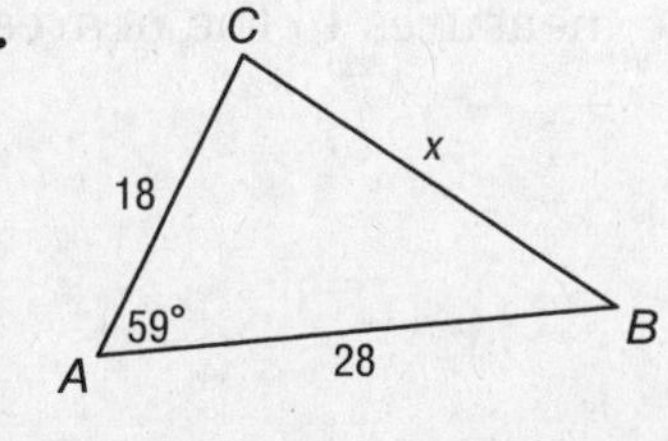

6.

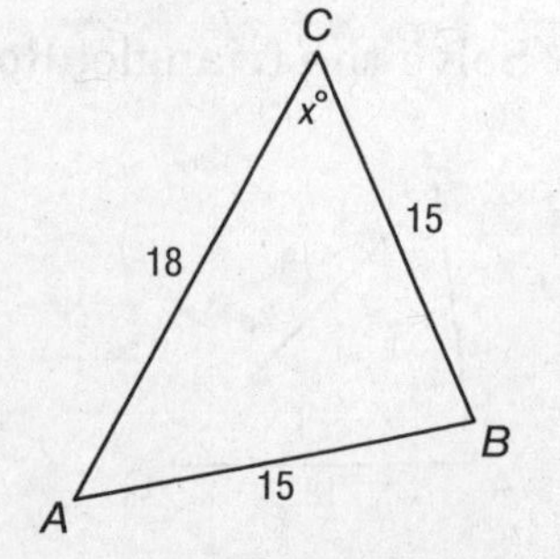

NAME ______________________ DATE ____________ PERIOD ____________

8-6 Skills Practice

The Law of Sines and Law of Cosines

Find x. Round angle measures to the nearest degree and side lengths to the nearest tenth.

1.

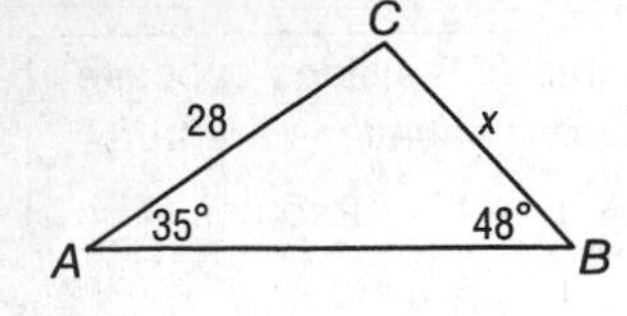

2.

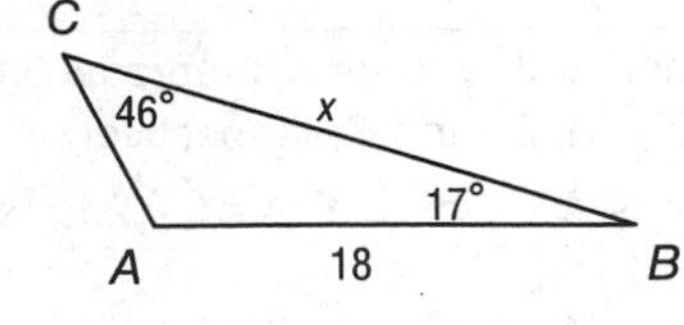

3.

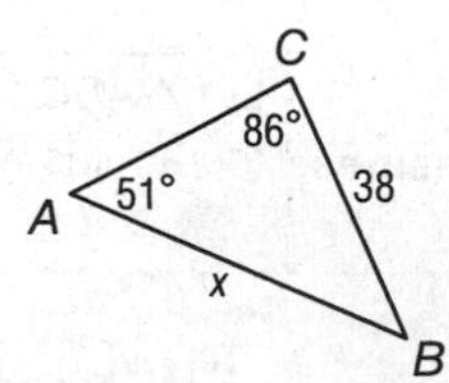

4.

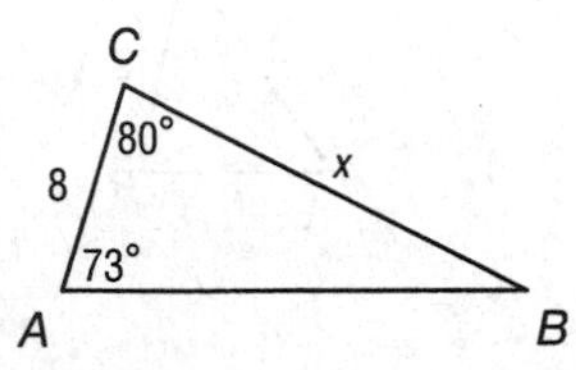

5.

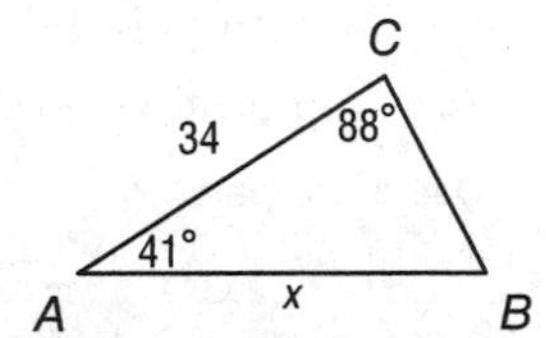

6.

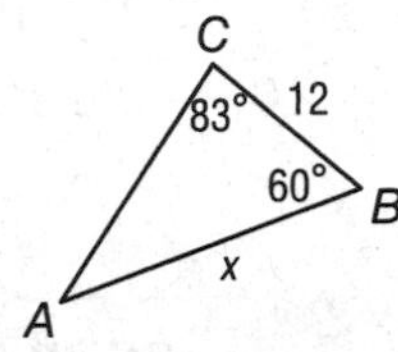

7.

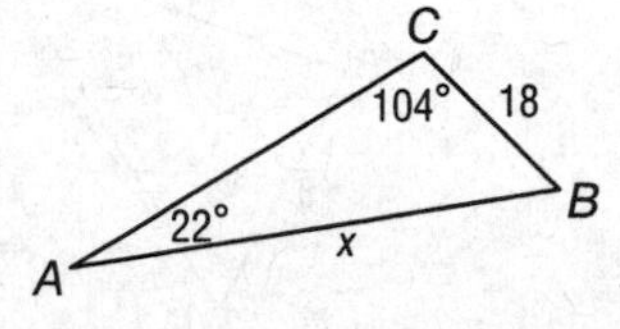

8.

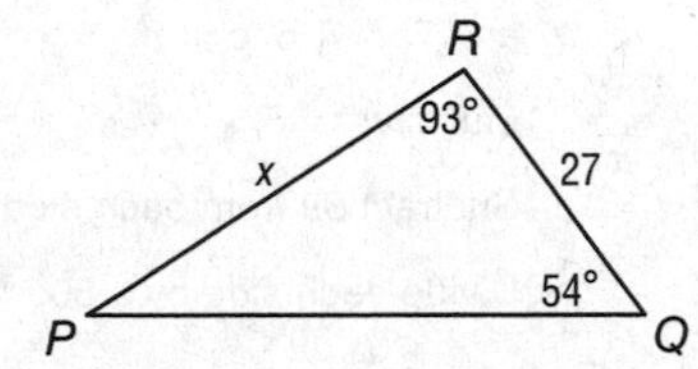

9.

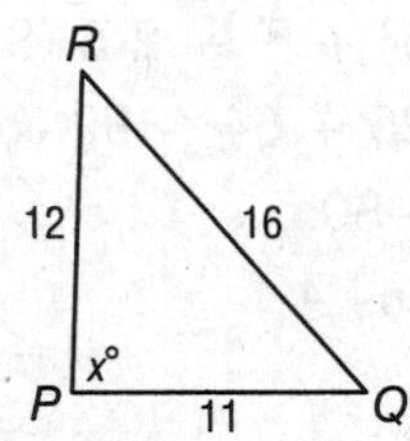

10.

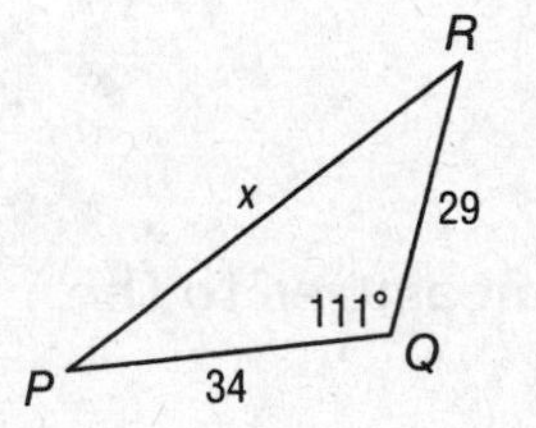

11.

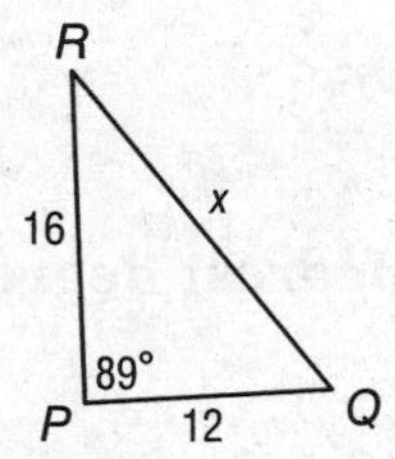

12.

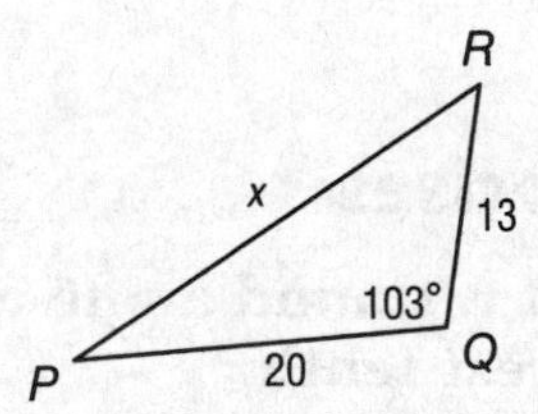

13.

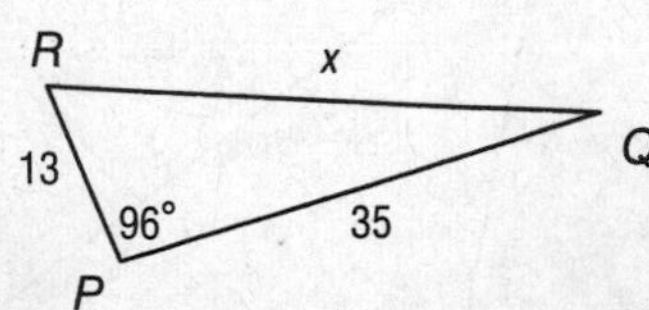

14.

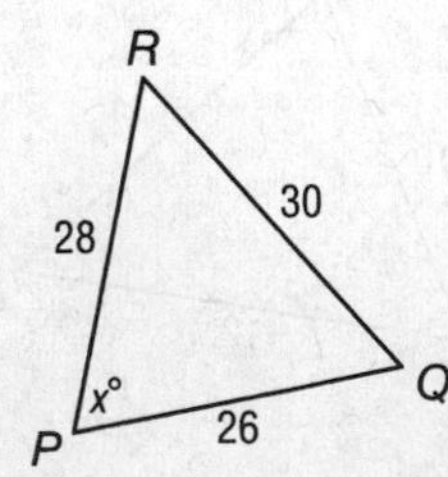

15.

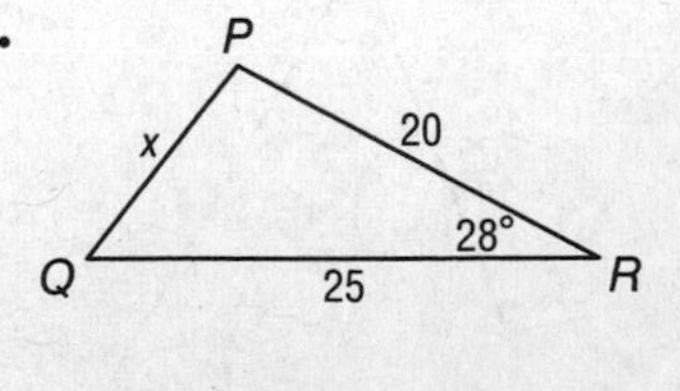

16. Solve the triangle. Round angle measures to the nearest degree.

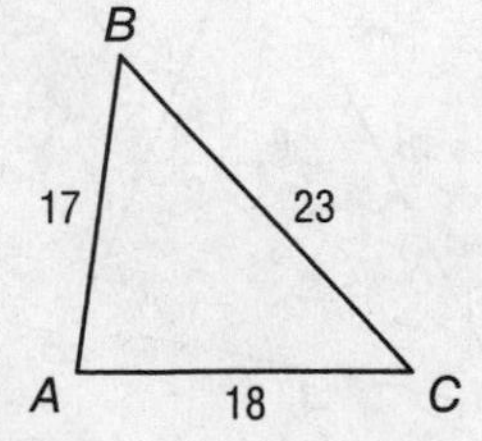

NAME ______________________ DATE __________ PERIOD __________

8-6 Practice

The Law of Sines and Law of Cosines

Find x. Round angle measures to the nearest degree and side lengths to the nearest tenth.

1.

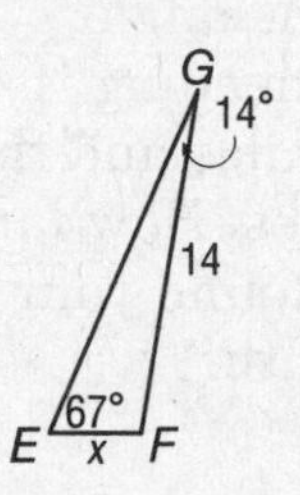

2.

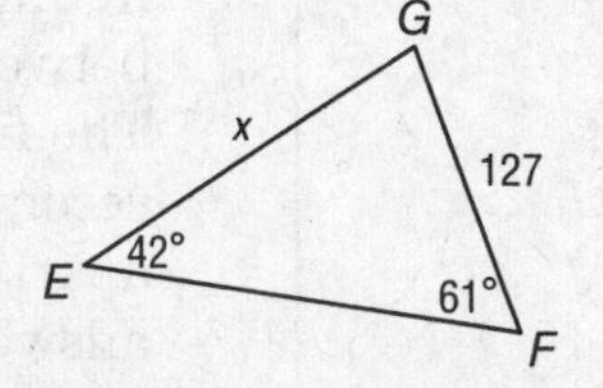

3.

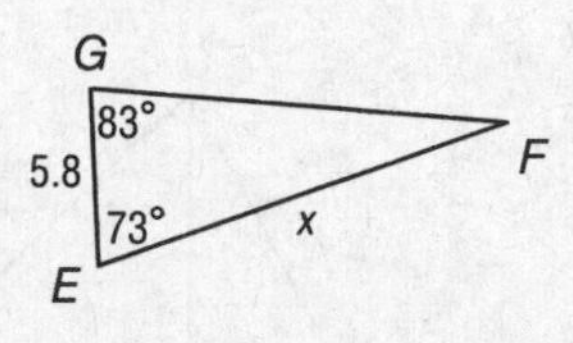

4.

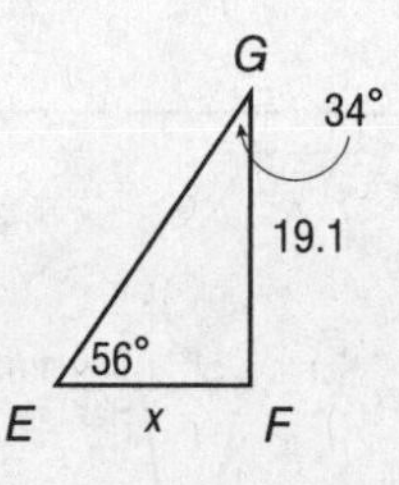

5.

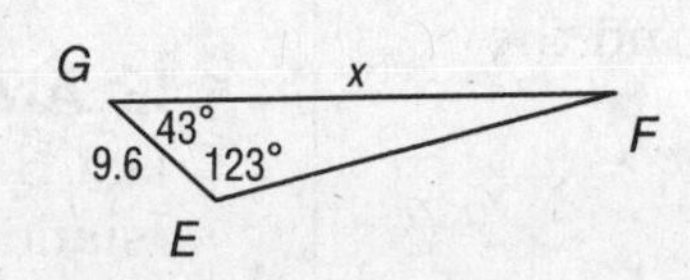

6.

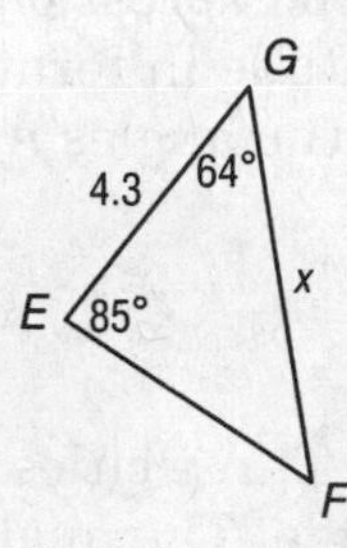

7.

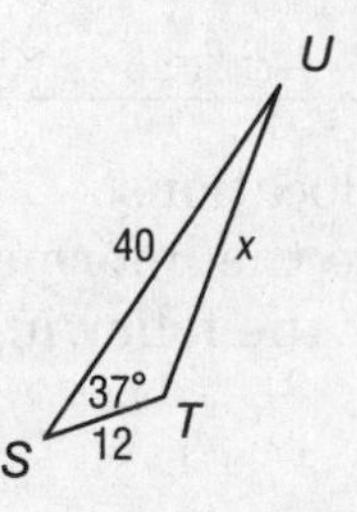

8.

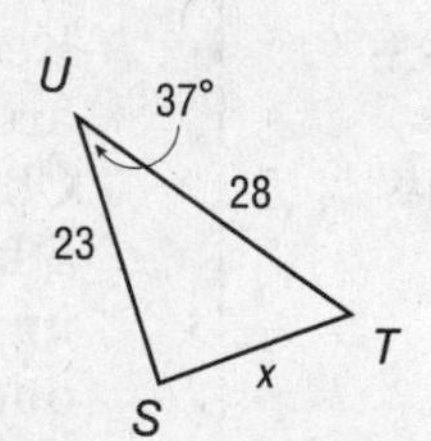

9.

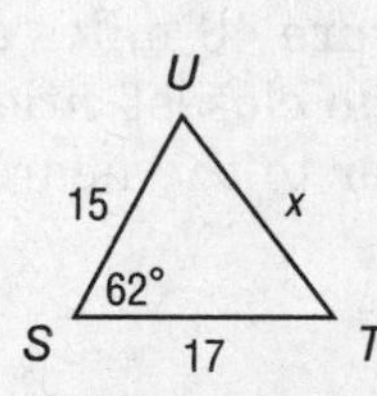

10.

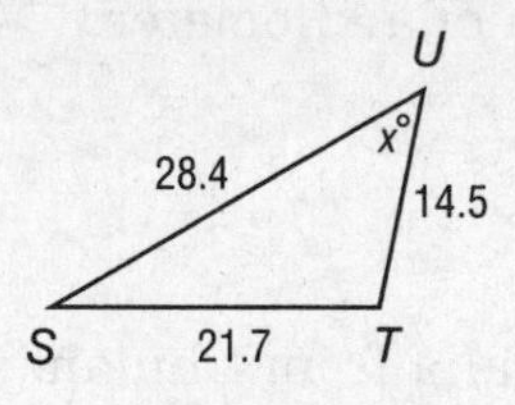

11.

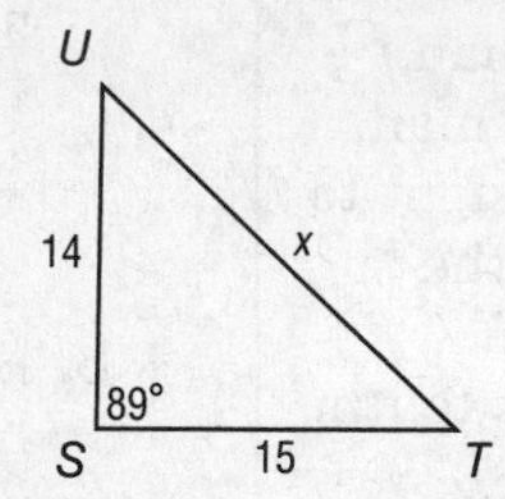

12.

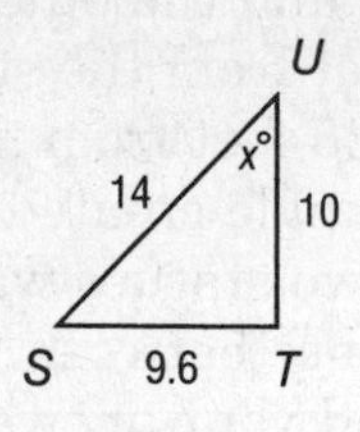

13. INDIRECT MEASUREMENT To find the distance from the edge of the lake to the tree on the island in the lake, Hannah set up a triangular configuration as shown in the diagram. The distance from location A to location B is 85 meters. The measures of the angles at A and B are 51° and 83°, respectively. What is the distance from the edge of the lake at B to the tree on the island at C?

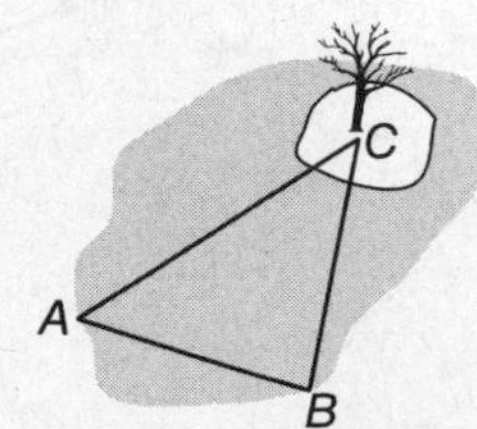

Lesson 8-6

NAME ______________________ DATE ____________ PERIOD ____________

8-6 Word Problem Practice

The Law of Sines and Law of Cosines

1. **ALTITUDES** In triangle ABC, the altitude to side $\overline{AB}$ is drawn.

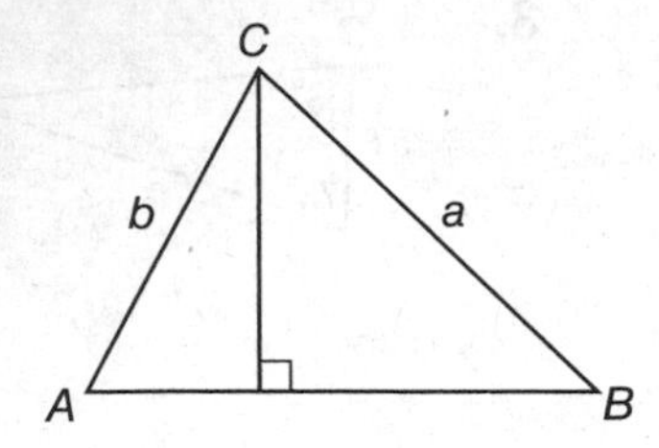

Give two expressions for the length of the altitude in terms of a, b, and the sine of the angles A and B.

2. **MAPS** Three cities form the vertices of a triangle. The angles of the triangle are 40°, 60°, and 80°. The two most distant cities are 40 miles apart. How close are the two closest cities? Round your answer to the nearest tenth of a mile.

3. **STATUES** Gail was visiting an art gallery. In one room, she stood so that she had a view of two statues, one of a man, and the other of a woman. She was 40 feet from the statue of the woman, and 35 feet from the statue of the man. The angle created by the lines of sight to the two statues was 21°. What is the distance between the two statues? Round your answer to the nearest tenth.

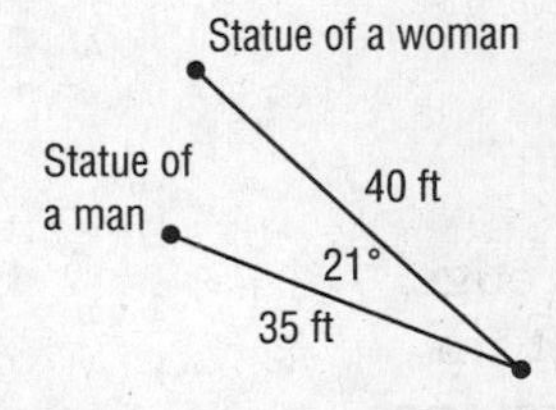

4. **CARS** Two cars start moving from the same location. They head straight, but in different directions. The angle between where they are heading is 43°. The first car travels 20 miles and the second car travels 37 miles. How far apart are the two cars? Round your answer to the nearest tenth.

5. **ISLANDS** Oahu is a Hawaiian Island. Off of the coast of Oahu, there is a very tiny island known as Chinaman's Hat. Keoki and Malia are observing Chinaman's Hat from locations 5 kilometers apart. Use the information in the figure to answer the following questions.

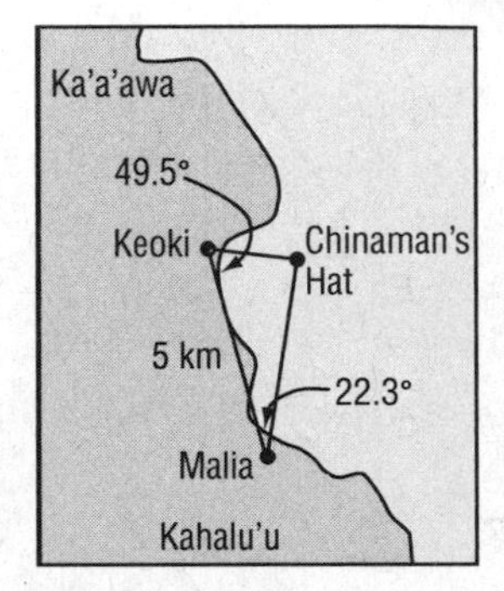

a. How far is Keoki from Chinaman's Hat? Round your answer to the nearest tenth of a kilometer.

b. How far is Malia from Chinaman's Hat? Round your answer to the nearest tenth of a kilometer.

NAME ______________________ DATE __________ PERIOD __________

8-6 Enrichment

Identities

An **identity** is an equation that is true for all values of the variable for which both sides are defined. One way to verify an identity is to use a right triangle and the definitions for trigonometric functions.

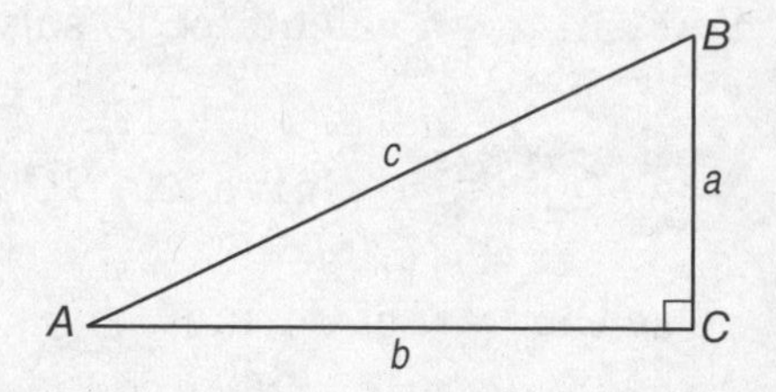

Example 1 **Verify that $(\sin A)^2 + (\cos A)^2 = 1$ is an identity.**

$$(\sin A)^2 + (\cos A)^2 = \left(\frac{a}{c}\right)^2 + \left(\frac{b}{c}\right)^2$$
$$= \frac{a^2 + b^2}{c^2} = \frac{c^2}{c^2} = 1$$

To check whether an equation *may* be an identity, you can test several values. However, since you cannot test all values, you cannot be *certain* that the equation is an identity.

Example 2 **Test $\sin 2x = 2 \sin x \cos x$ to see if it could be an identity.**

Try $x = 20$. Use a calculator to evaluate each expression.

$\sin 2x = \sin 40$
≈ 0.643

$2 \sin x \cos x = 2 (\sin 20)(\cos 20)$
$\approx 2(0.342)(0.940)$
≈ 0.643

Since the left and right sides seem equal, the equation may be an identity.

Exercises

Use triangle *ABC* shown above. Verify that each equation is an identity.

1. $\dfrac{\cos A}{\sin A} = \dfrac{1}{\tan A}$

2. $\dfrac{\tan B}{\sin B} = \dfrac{1}{\cos B}$

3. $\tan B \cos B = \sin B$

4. $1 - (\cos B)^2 = (\sin B)^2$

Try several values for x to test whether each equation could be an identity.

5. $\cos 2x = (\cos x)^2 - (\sin x)^2$

6. $\cos (90 - x) = \sin x$

NAME ______________________ DATE __________ PERIOD __________

8-6 Graphing Calculator Activity

Solving Triangles Using the Law of Sines or Cosines

You can use a calculator to solve triangles using the Law of Sines or Cosines.

Example **Solve $\triangle ABC$ if $a = 6$, $b = 2$, and $c = 7.5$.**

Use the Law of Cosines.

$a^2 = b^2 + c^2 - 2bc \cos A$

$6^2 = 2^2 + 7.5^2 - 2(2)(7.5) \cos A$

$m\angle A = \cos^{-1} \frac{6^2 - 2^2 - 7.5^2}{-2(2)(7.5)}$ Use your calculator to find the measure of $\angle A$.

Keystrokes: [2nd] [COS⁻¹] [(] 6 [x²] [−] 2 [x²] [−] 7.5 [x²] [)] [÷] [(] [(−)] 2 [×] 2 [×] 7.5 [)] [)] [ENTER] 36.06658826

So $m\angle A \approx 36$. Use the Law of Sines and your calculator to find $m\angle B$.

$\frac{\sin A}{a} = \frac{\sin B}{b}$

$\frac{\sin 36}{6} \approx \frac{\sin B}{2}$

$m\angle B \approx \sin^{-1} \frac{2 \sin 36°}{6}$

Keystrokes: [2nd] [SIN⁻¹] [(] 2 [SIN] 36 [)] [÷] 6 [)] [ENTER] 11.29896425

So $m\angle B \approx 11$. By the Triangle Angle-Sum Theorem, $m\angle C \approx 180 - (36 + 11)$ or 133.

Exercises

Solve each $\triangle ABC$. Round measures of sides to the nearest tenth and measures of angles to the nearest degree.

1. $a = 9$, $b = 14$, $c = 12$

2. $m\angle C = 80$, $c = 9$, $m\angle A = 40$

3. $m\angle B = 45$, $m\angle C = 56$, $a = 2$

4. $a = 5.7$, $b = 6$, $c = 5$

5. $a = 11$, $b = 15$, $c = 21$

8-7 Study Guide and Intervention

Vectors

Geometric Vector Operations A vector is a directed segment representing a quantity that has both **magnitude,** or length, and **direction.** For example, the speed and direction of an airplane can be represented by a vector. In symbols, a vector is written as $\overrightarrow{AB}$, where A is the initial point and B is the endpoint, or as $\vec{v}$. The sum of two vectors is called the **resultant.** Subtracting a vector is equivalent to adding its opposite. The resultant of two vectors can be found using the **parallelogram method** or the **triangle method.**

Example **Copy the vectors to find $\vec{a} - \vec{b}$.**

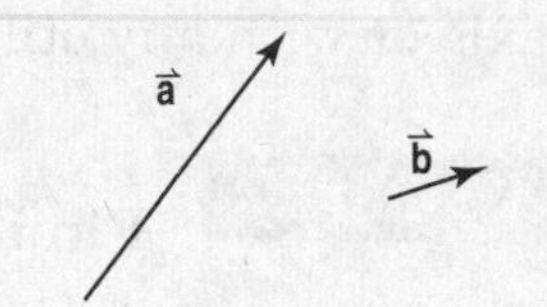

Method 1: Use the parallelogram method.

Copy $\vec{a}$ and $-\vec{b}$ with the same initial point.	Complete the parallelogram.	Draw the diagonal of the parallelogram from the initial point.
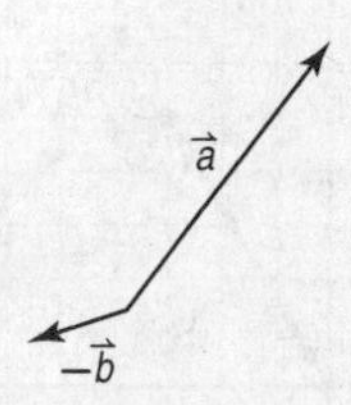	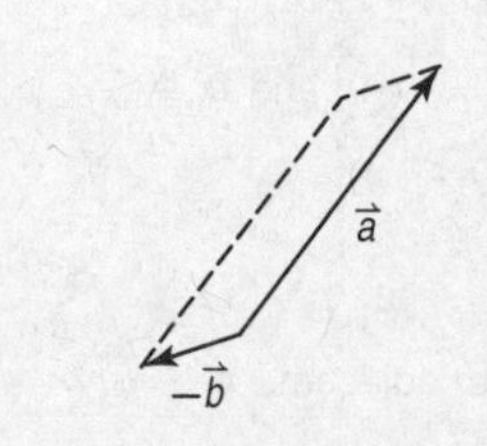	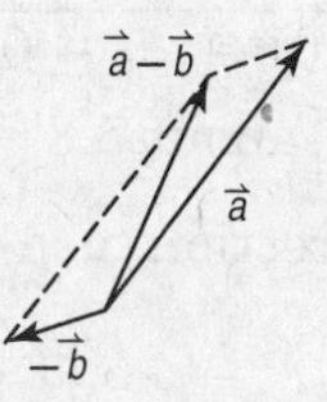

Method 2: Use the triangle method.

Copy $\vec{a}$.	Place the initial point of $-\vec{b}$ at the terminal point of $\vec{a}$.	Draw the vector from the initial point of $\vec{a}$ to the terminal point of $-\vec{b}$.
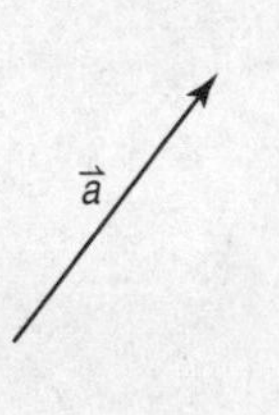	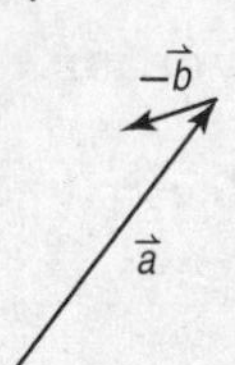	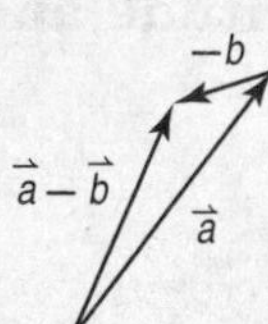

Exercises

Copy the vectors. Then find each sum or difference.

1. $\vec{c} + \vec{d}$

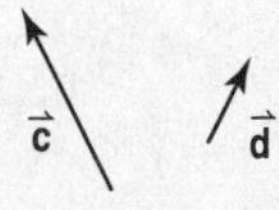

2. $\vec{w} - \vec{z}$

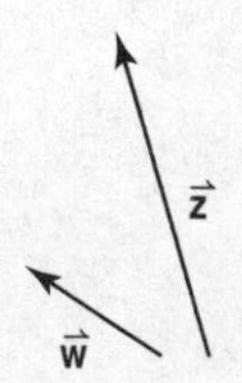

3. $\vec{a} - \vec{b}$

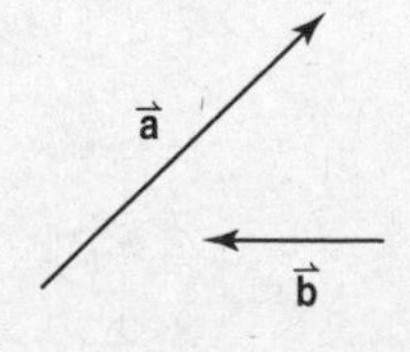

4. $\vec{r} + \vec{t}$

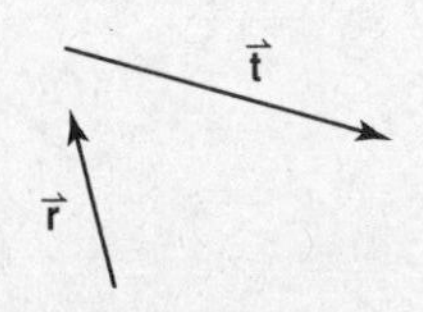

8-7 Study Guide and Intervention *(continued)*

Vectors

Vectors on the Coordinate Plane A vector in **standard position** has its initial point at (0, 0) and can be represented by the ordered pair for point B. The vector at the right can be expressed as $\vec{v} = \langle 5, 3 \rangle$. You can use the Distance Formula to find the magnitude $|\overrightarrow{AB}|$ of a vector. You can describe the direction of a vector by measuring the angle that the vector forms with the positive x-axis or with any other horizontal line.

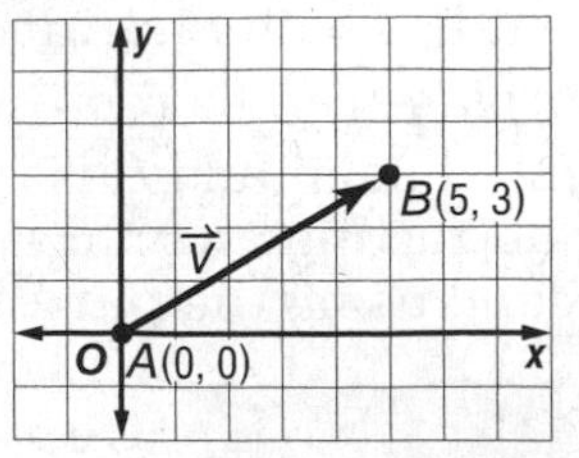

Example **Find the magnitude and direction of $\vec{a} = \langle 3, 5 \rangle$.**

Find the magnitude.

$\vec{a} = \sqrt{(x_2 - x_1)^2 + (y_2 - y_1)^2}$ Distance Formula

$= \sqrt{(3 - 0)^2 + (5 - 0)^2}$ $(x_1, y_1) = (0, 0)$ and $(x_2, y_2) = (3, 5)$

$= \sqrt{34}$ or about 5.8 Simplify.

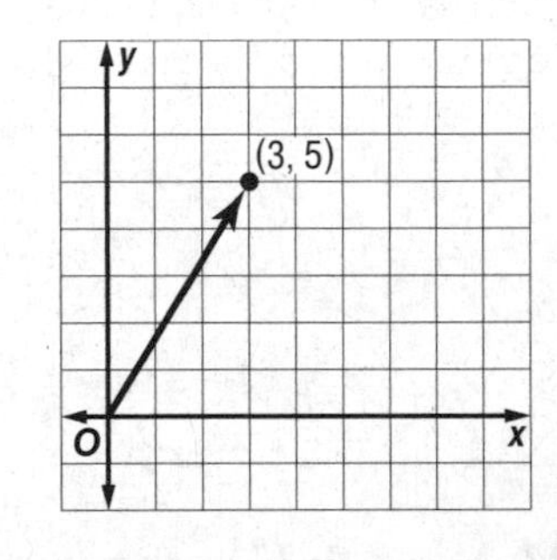

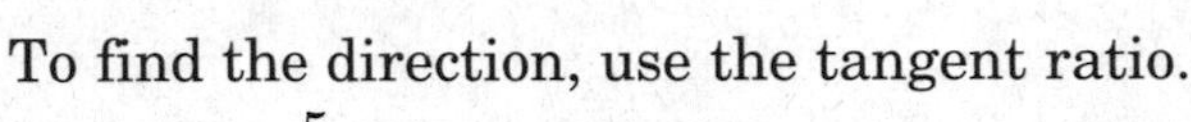

To find the direction, use the tangent ratio.

$\tan \theta = \frac{5}{3}$ The tangent ratio is opposite over adjacent.

$m\angle\theta \approx 59.0$ Use a calculator.

The magnitude of the vector is about 5.8 units and its direction is 59°.

Exercises

Find the magnitude and direction of each vector.

1. $\vec{b} = \langle -5, 2 \rangle$

2. $\vec{c} = \langle -2, 1 \rangle$

3. $\vec{d} = \langle 3, 4 \rangle$

4. $\vec{m} = \langle 5, -1 \rangle$

5. $\vec{r} = \langle -3, -4 \rangle$

6. $\vec{v} = \langle -4, 1 \rangle$

8-7 Skills Practice

Vectors

Use a ruler and a protractor to draw each vector. Include a scale on each diagram.

1. $\vec{a}$ = 20 meters per second 60° west of south

2. $\vec{b}$ = 10 pound of force at 135° to the horizontal

Copy the vectors to find each sum or difference.

3. $\vec{a} + \vec{z}$

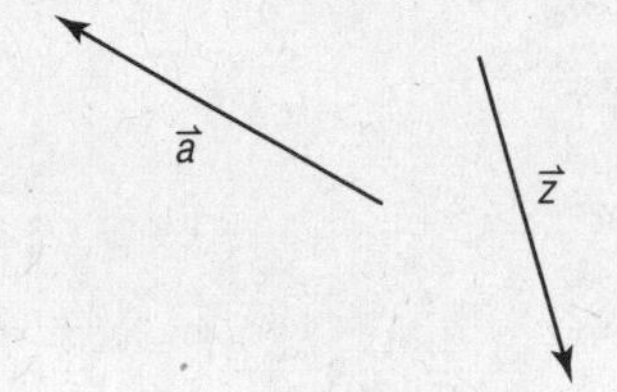

4. $\vec{t} - \vec{r}$

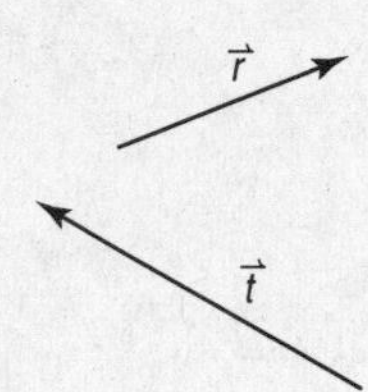

Write the component form of each vector.

5.

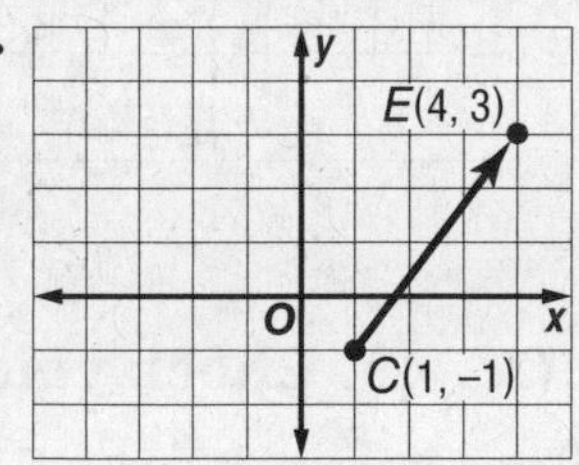

6.

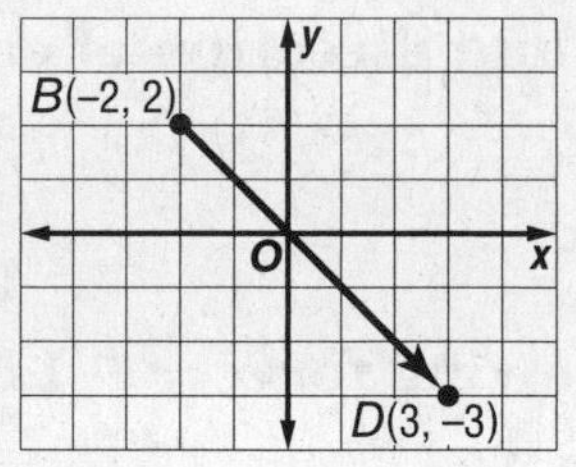

Find the magnitude and direction of each vector.

7. $\vec{m} = \langle 2, 12 \rangle$

8. $\vec{k} = \langle -8, -3 \rangle$

9. $\vec{f} = \langle -5, 11 \rangle$

Find each of the following for $\vec{a} = \langle 2, 4 \rangle$, $\vec{b} = \langle 3, -3 \rangle$, and $\vec{c} = \langle 4, -1 \rangle$. Check your answers graphically.

10. $2\vec{a} + \vec{b}$

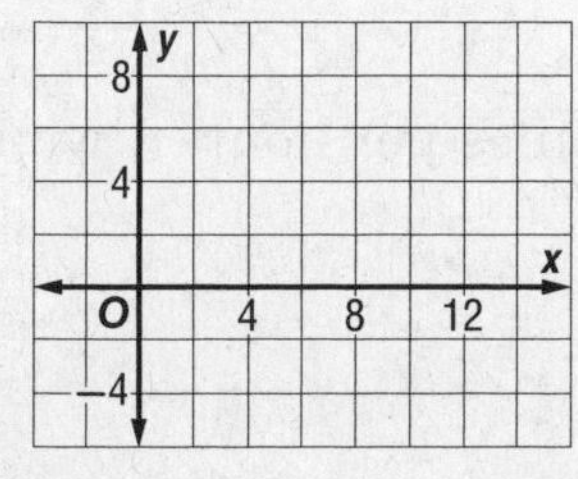

11. $\vec{b} - 2\vec{c}$

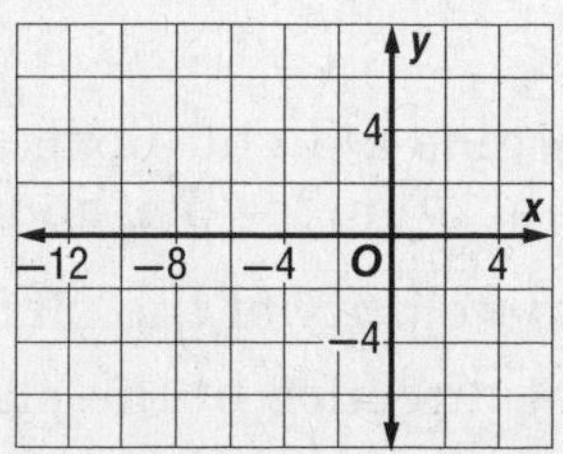

NAME ____________________ DATE __________ PERIOD __________

8-7 Practice

Vectors

Use a ruler and a protractor to draw each vector. Include a scale on each diagram.

1. $\vec{v}$ = 12 Newtons of force at 40° to the horizontal

2. $\vec{w}$ = 15 miles per hour 70° east of north

Copy the vectors to find each sum or difference.

3. $\vec{p} + \vec{r}$

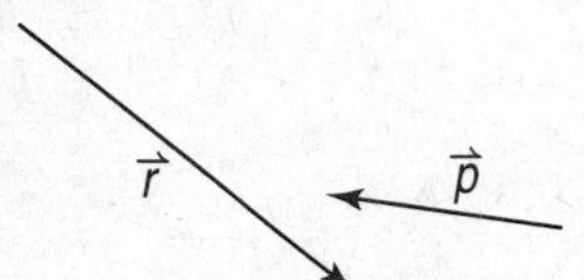

4. $\vec{a} - \vec{b}$

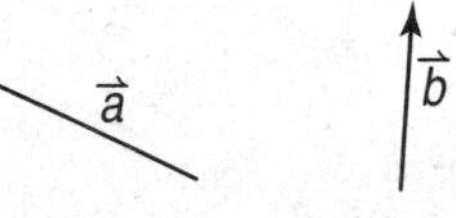

5. Write the component form of $\overrightarrow{AB}$.

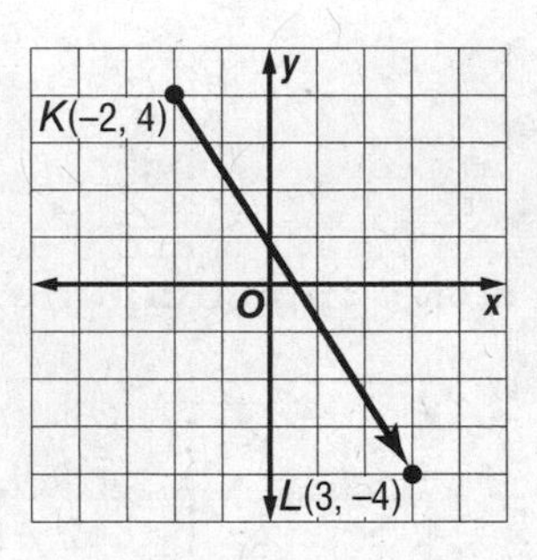

Find the magnitude and direction of each vector.

6. $\vec{t} = \langle 6, 11 \rangle$

7. $\vec{g} = \langle 9, -7 \rangle$

Find each of the following for $\vec{a} = \langle -1.5, 4 \rangle$, $\vec{b} = \langle 7, 3 \rangle$, and $\vec{c} = \langle 1, -2 \rangle$. Check your answers graphically.

8. $2\vec{a} + \vec{b}$

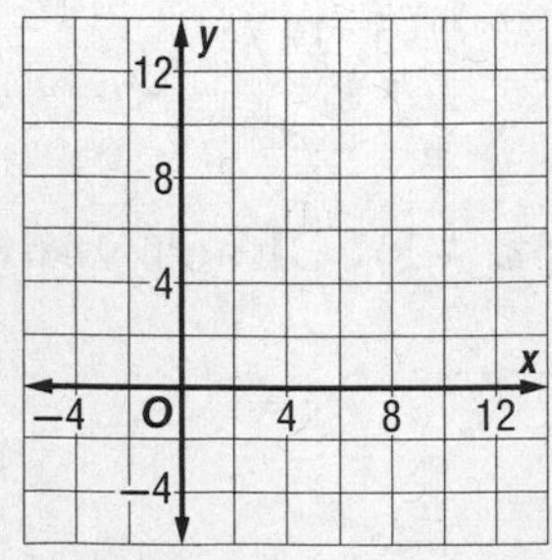

9. $2\vec{c} - \vec{b}$

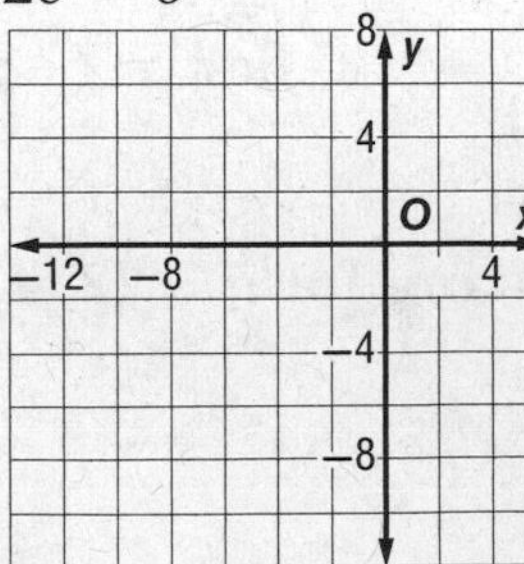

10. AVIATION A jet begins a flight along a path due north at 300 miles per hour. A wind is blowing due west at 30 miles per hour.

a. Find the resultant velocity of the plane.

b. Find the resultant direction of the plane.

8-7 Word Problem Practice

Vectors

1. WIND The vector $\vec{v}$ represents the speed and direction that the wind is blowing. Suddenly the wind picks up and doubles its speed, but the direction does not change. Write an expression for a vector that describes the new wind velocity in terms of $\vec{v}$.

2. SWIMMING Jan is swimming in a triathlon event. When the ocean water is still, her velocity can be represented by the vector $\langle 2, 1 \rangle$ miles per hour. During the competition, there was a fierce current represented by the vector $\langle -1, -1 \rangle$ miles per hour. What vector represents Jan's velocity during the race?

3. POLYGONS Draw a regular polygon around the origin. For each side of the polygon, associate a vector whose magnitude is the length of the corresponding side and whose direction points in the clockwise motion around the origin. What vector represents the sum of all these vectors? Explain.

4. BASEBALL Rick is in the middle of a baseball game. His teammate throws him the ball, but throws it far in front of him. He has to run as fast as he can to catch it. As he runs, he knows that as soon as he catches it, he has to throw it as hard as he can to the teammate at home plate. He has no time to stop. In the figure, $\vec{x}$ is the vector that represents the velocity of the ball *after* Rick throws it and $\vec{v}$ represents Rick's velocity because he is running. Assume that Rick can throw just as hard when running as he can when standing still.

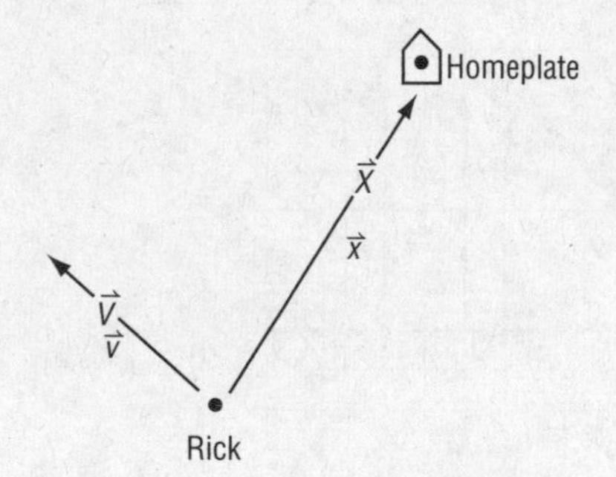

a. What vector would represent the velocity of the ball if Rick threw it the same way but he was standing still?

b. The angle between $\vec{x}$ and $\vec{v}$ is 89°. By running, did it help Rick get the ball to home plate faster than he would have normally been able to if he were standing still?

Lesson 8-7

NAME ______________________ DATE __________ PERIOD __________

8-7 Enrichment

Dot Product

The dot product of two vectors represents how much the vectors point in the direction of each other. If $\vec{v}$ is a vector represented by $\langle a, b \rangle$ and $\vec{u}$ is a vector represented by $\langle c, d \rangle$, the formula to find the dot product is:

$\vec{v} \cdot \vec{u} = ac + bd$

Look at the following example:

Graph the vectors and find the dot product of $\vec{v}$ and $\vec{u}$ if $\vec{v} = \langle 3, -1 \rangle$ and $\vec{u} = \langle 2, 5 \rangle$.

$\vec{v} \cdot \vec{u} = (3)(2) + (-1)(5)$ or 1

Graph the vectors and find the dot products.

1. $\vec{v} = \langle 2, 1 \rangle$ and $\vec{u} = \langle -4, 2 \rangle$

The dot product is ______

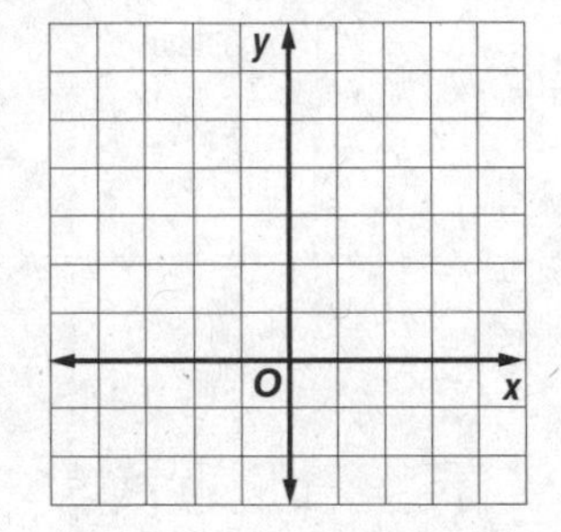

2. $\vec{v} = \langle 3, -2 \rangle$ and $\vec{u} = \langle 1, 4 \rangle$

The dot product is ______

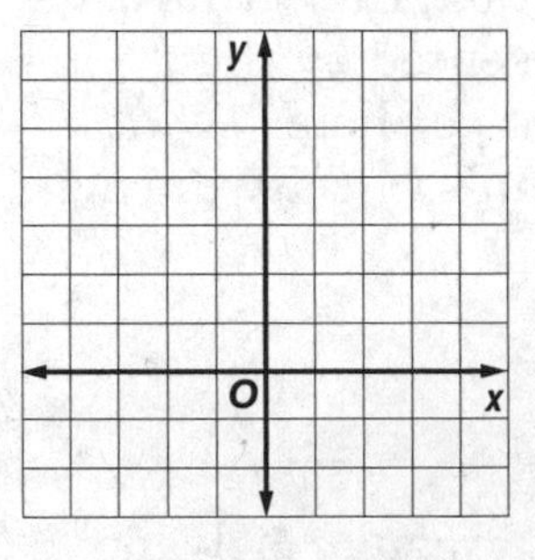

3. $\vec{v} = \langle 0, 3 \rangle$ and $\vec{u} = \langle 2, 4 \rangle$

The dot product is ______

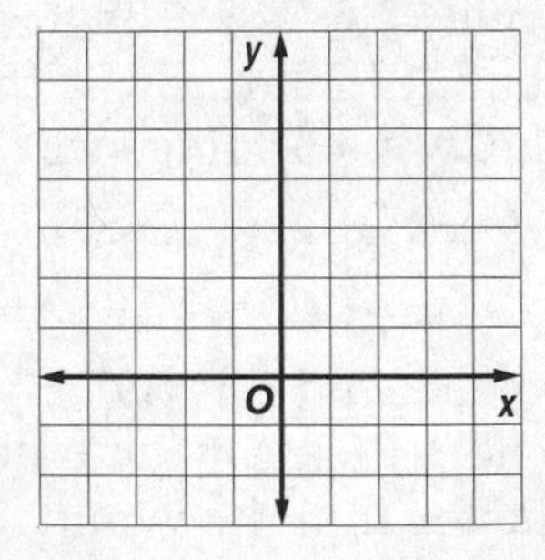

4. $\vec{v} = \langle -1, 4 \rangle$ and $\vec{u} = \langle -4, 2 \rangle$

The dot product is ______

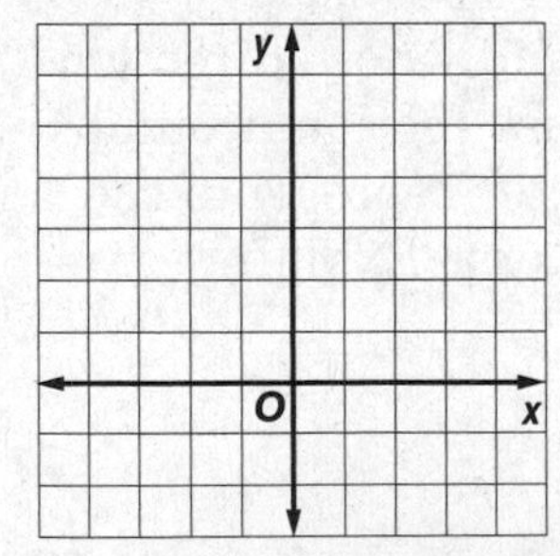

5. Notice the angle formed by the two vectors and the corresponding dot product. Is there any relationship between the type of angle between the two vectors and the sign of the dot product? Make a conjecture.

8 Student Recording Sheet

Use this recording sheet with pages 610–611 of the Student Edition.

Assessment

Multiple Choice

Read each question. Then fill in the correct answer.

1. Ⓐ Ⓑ Ⓒ Ⓓ
2. Ⓕ Ⓖ Ⓗ Ⓙ
3. Ⓐ Ⓑ Ⓒ Ⓓ
4. Ⓕ Ⓖ Ⓗ Ⓙ
5. Ⓐ Ⓑ Ⓒ Ⓓ
6. Ⓕ Ⓖ Ⓗ Ⓙ

Short Response/Gridded Response

Record your answer in the blank.

For gridded response questions, also enter your answer in the grid by writing each number or symbol in a box. Then fill in the corresponding circle for that number or symbol.

7. ______________ *(grid in)*
8. ______________
9. ______________
10. ______________ *(grid in)*
11. ______________
12. ______________
13. ______________
14. ______________

7.

	⊘	⊘	⊘	
⊙	⊙	⊙	⊙	⊙
0	0	0	0	0
1	1	1	1	1
2	2	2	2	2
3	3	3	3	3
4	4	4	4	4
5	5	5	5	5
6	6	6	6	6
7	7	7	7	7
8	8	8	8	8
9	9	9	9	9

10.

	⊘	⊘	⊘	
⊙	⊙	⊙	⊙	⊙
0	0	0	0	0
1	1	1	1	1
2	2	2	2	2
3	3	3	3	3
4	4	4	4	4
5	5	5	5	5
6	6	6	6	6
7	7	7	7	7
8	8	8	8	8
9	9	9	9	9

Extended Response

Record your answers for Question 15 on the back of this paper.

NAME ______________________________ DATE ____________ PERIOD ____________

8 Rubric for Scoring Extended-Response

General Scoring Guidelines

- If a student gives only a correct numerical answer to a problem but does not show how he or she arrived at the answer, the student will be awarded only 1 credit. All extended-response questions require the student to show work.
- A fully correct answer for a multiple-part question requires correct responses for all parts of the question. For example, if a question has three parts, the correct response to one or two parts of the question that required work to be shown is not considered a fully correct response.
- Students who use trial and error to solve a problem must show their method. Merely showing that the answer checks or is correct is not considered a complete response for full credit.

Exercise 15 Rubric

Score	Specific Criteria
4	The values of $x = 10$, $y = 16$, and $z = 12.8$ are found using appropriate proportions based upon students knowledge of right triangle geometric mean theorems.
3	A generally correct solution, but may contain minor flaws in reasoning or computation.
2	A partially correct interpretation and/or solution to the problem.
1	A correct solution with no evidence or explanation.
0	An incorrect solution indicating no mathematical understanding of the concept or task, or no solution is given.

NAME ______________________ DATE __________ PERIOD __________

8 Chapter 8 Quiz 1

SCORE ______

(Lessons 8-1 and 8-2)

1. Find the geometric mean between 12 and 16. — 1. ______

For Questions 2 and 3, find *x* and *y*.

2.

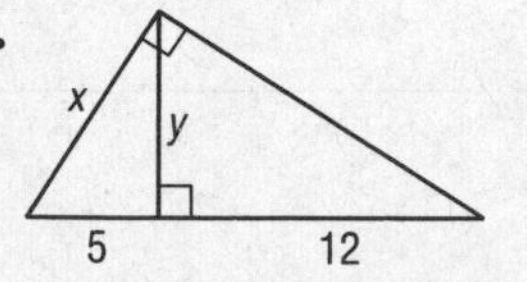

3.

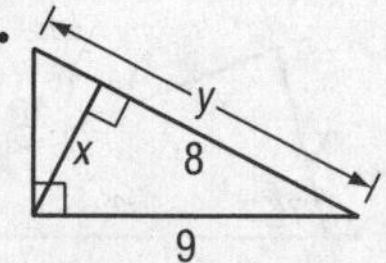

2. ______

3. ______

4. Find x.

4. ______

5. The measures of the sides of a triangle are 19, 15, and 13. Use the Pythagorean Theorem to classify the triangle as *acute*, *obtuse*, or *right*. — 5. ______

NAME ______________________ DATE __________ PERIOD __________

8 Chapter 8 Quiz 2

SCORE ______

(Lessons 8-3 and 8-4)

For Questions 1 and 2, find *x*.

1.

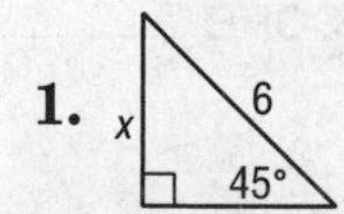

2.

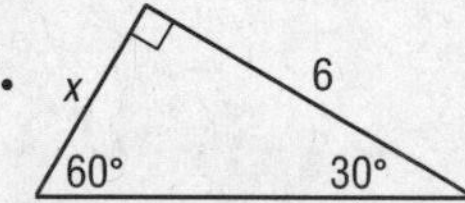

1. ______

2. ______

For Questions 3 and 4, find *x* to the nearest tenth.

3.

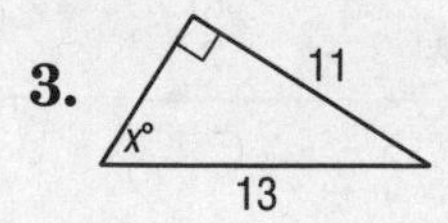

4.

3. ______

4. ______

5. A rectangle has a diagonal 20 inches long that forms angles of 60° and 30° with the sides. Find the perimeter of the rectangle. — 5. ______

6. Find sin 52°. Round to the nearest ten-thousandth. — 6. ______

7. If $\cos A = 0.8945$, find $m\angle A$ to the nearest degree. — 7. ______

8. The distance along a hill is 24 feet. If the land slopes uphill at an angle of 8°, find the vertical distance from the top to the bottom of the hill. Round to the nearest tenth. — 8. ______

9. Use a calculator to find the measure of $\angle T$ to the nearest tenth.

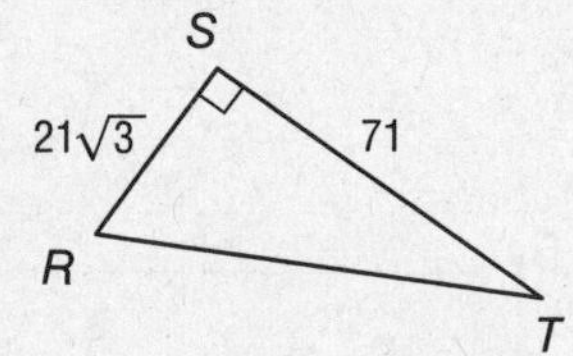

10. Use a calculator to find the measure of $\angle T$ to the nearest tenth.

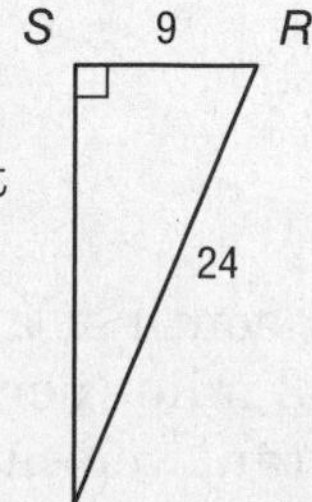

9. ______

10. ______

Assessment

NAME ______________________ DATE ____________ PERIOD ____________

8 Chapter 8 Quiz 3

SCORE ________

(Lessons 8-5 and 8-6)

1. Name the angle of elevation in the figure.

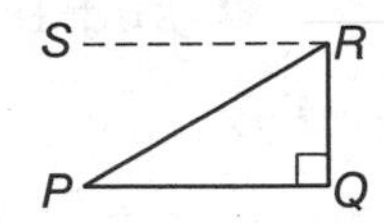

1. ____________________

2. Find x to the nearest tenth.

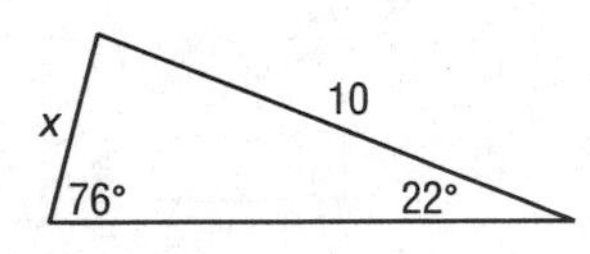

2. ____________________

3. Solve $\triangle ABC$. Round angle measures to the nearest degree and side measures to the nearest tenth.

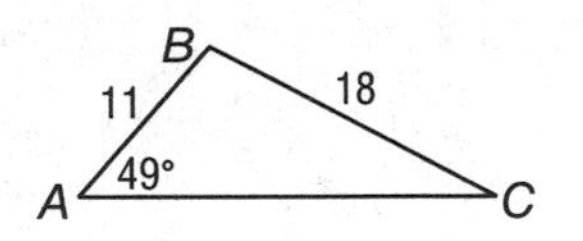

3. ____________________

4. Solve $\triangle RST$. Round your answers to the nearest degree.

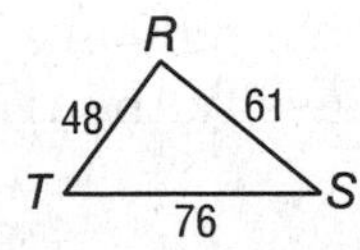

4. ____________________

5. A squirrel, 37 feet up in a tree, sees a dog 29 feet from the base of the tree. Find the measure of the angle of depression to the nearest degree.

5. ____________________

NAME ______________________ DATE ____________ PERIOD ____________

8 Chapter 8 Quiz 4

SCORE ________

(Lesson 8-7)

Find the magnitude and direction of each vector.

1. $\overrightarrow{RT}$: $R(14, 6)$ and $T(-5, -10)$ **1.** ____________________

2. $\overrightarrow{PQ}$: $P(20, -16)$ and $Q(-9, -4)$ **2.** ____________________

Copy the vectors to find each sum or difference.

3. $\vec{c} + \vec{d}$ **4.** $\vec{k} - \vec{m}$ **3.** ____________________

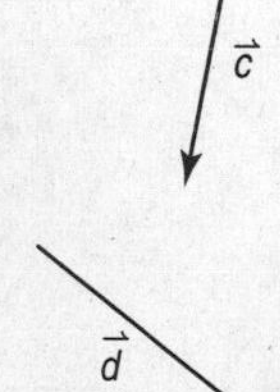

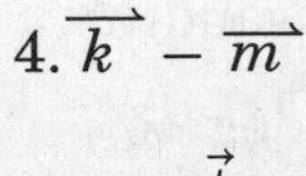

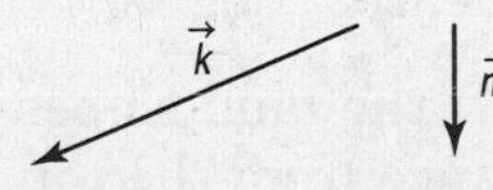

4. ____________________

5. Lidia is rollerblading south at a velocity of 9 miles per hour. The wind is blowing 3 miles per hour in the opposite direction. What is Lidia's resultant velocity and direction? **5.** ____________________

NAME ______________________ DATE __________ PERIOD __________

8 Chapter 8 Mid-Chapter Test

SCORE ______

(Lessons 8-1 through 8-4)

Part I **Write the letter for the correct answer in the blank at the right of each question.**

1. Find the geometric mean between 7 and 9.

A $3\sqrt{7}$ **B** 16 **C** 8 **D** 2 **1.** ______

2. Find x.

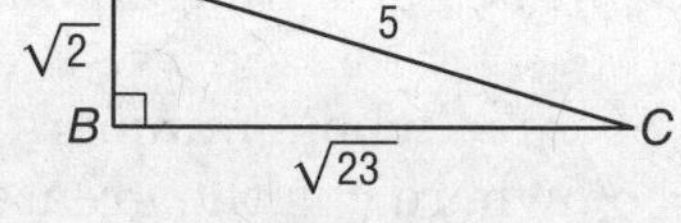

F $6\sqrt{6}$ **H** $6\sqrt{55}$

G $\frac{\sqrt{2}}{5}$ **J** $\frac{\sqrt{23}}{5}$ **2.** ______

3. Find sin C.

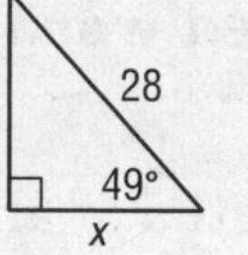

A $\sqrt{2}$ **C** $\frac{\sqrt{23}}{\sqrt{2}}$

B $\frac{\sqrt{2}}{5}$ **D** $\frac{\sqrt{23}}{5}$ **3.** ______

4. Find x to the nearest tenth.

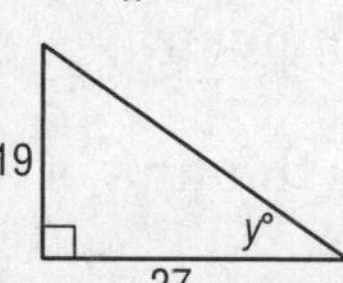

F 14 **H** 18.4

G 21.1 **J** 32.2 **4.** ______

5. Find y to the nearest degree.

A 145 **C** 45

B 60 **D** 35 **5.** ______

19
y°
27

Part II

For Questions 6–8, find x and y.

6.

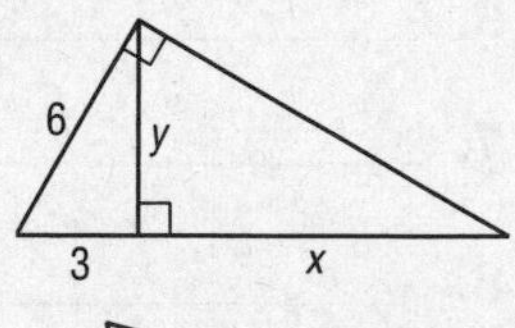

7.

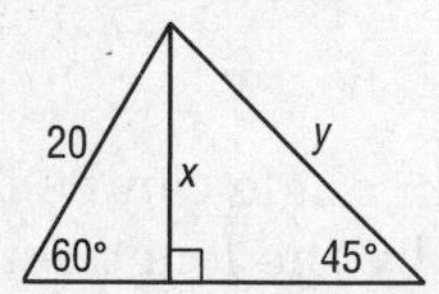

6. ______

7. ______

8.

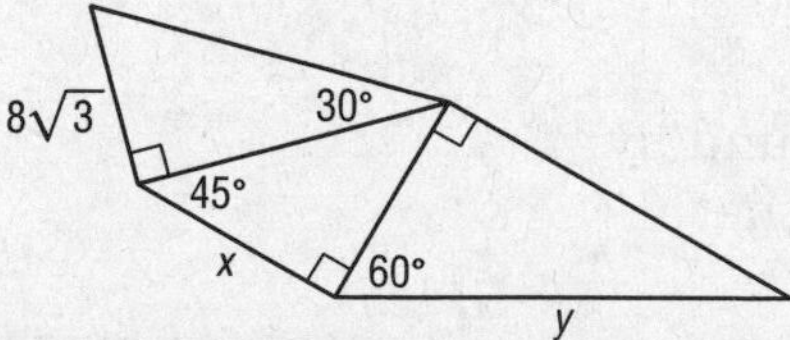

8. ______

9. The measures of the sides of a triangle are 56, 90, and 106. Use the Pythagorean Theorem to classify the triangle as *acute*, *obtuse*, or *right*. **9.** ______

10. Guy wires 80 feet long support a 65-foot tall telephone pole. To the nearest degree, what angle will the wires make with the ground? **10.** ______

Assessment

NAME ______________________ DATE __________ PERIOD __________

8 Chapter 8 Vocabulary Test

SCORE ______

angle of depression	inverse sine	sine
angle of elevation	inverse tangent	standard position
component form	Law of Cosines	tangent
cosine	Law of Sines	trigonometric ratio
direction	magnitude	trigonometry
geometric mean	Pythagorean Triple	vector
inverse cosine	resultant	

Choose the correct word to complete each sentence.

1. The square root of the product of two numbers is the (*geometric mean,* or *Pythagorean triple*) of the numbers. 1. __________

2. A group of three whole numbers that satisfy the equation $a^2 + b^2 = c^2$, where c is the greatest number, is called a (*trigonometric ratio,* or *Pythagorean triple*). 2. __________

Write whether each sentence is *true* or *false*. If false, replace the underlined word or number to make a true sentence.

3. The ratio of the lengths of any two sides of a right triangle is called a <u>geometric mean</u>. 3. __________

4. An angle between the line of sight and the horizontal when an observer looks upward is called a <u>angle of elevation</u>. 4. __________

Choose from the terms above to complete each sentence.

5. An angle between the line of sight and the horizontal when an observer looks downward is called a(n) ___?___. 5. __________

6. The word ___?___ is derived from the Greek term for triangle and measure. 6. __________

7. In a right triangle, the ___?___ of an angle can be found by dividing the length of the opposite leg by the length of the triangle's hypotenuse. 7. __________

8. In a right triangle, the ___?___ of an angle can be found by dividing the length of the opposite leg by the length of the adjacent leg. 8. __________

9. __________

Define each term in your own words.

9. component form

10. Pythagorean Theorem

10. __________

NAME _______________ DATE _______ PERIOD _______

8 Chapter 8 Test, Form 1

SCORE _______

Write the letter for the correct answer in the blank at the right of each question.

1. Find the geometric mean between 20 and 5.
A 100 **B** 50 **C** 12.5 **D** 10 **1.** _____

2. Find x in $\triangle ABC$.
F 8 **H** $\sqrt{20}$
G 10 **J** 64 **2.** _____

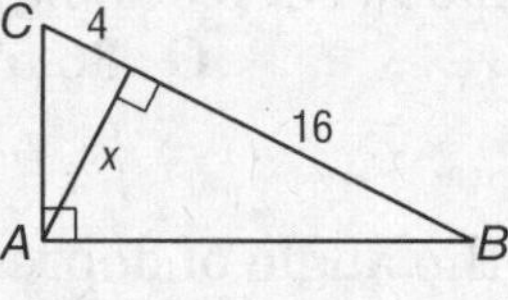

3. Find x in $\triangle PQR$.
A 13 **C** 16
B 15 **D** $\sqrt{60}$ **3.** _____

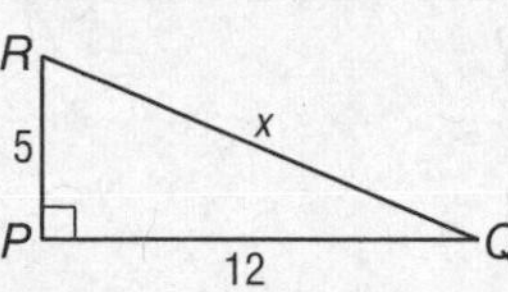

4. Find x in $\triangle STU$.
F 2 **H** $\sqrt{32}$
G 8 **J** $\sqrt{514}$ **4.** _____

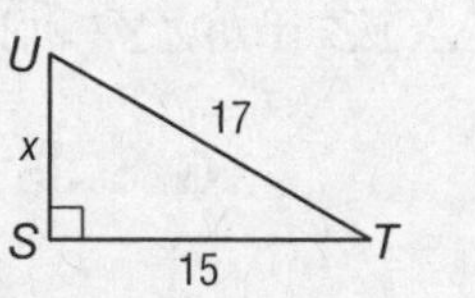

5. Which set of measures could represent the lengths of the sides of a right triangle?
A 2, 3, 4 **C** 8, 10, 12
B 7, 11, 14 **D** 9, 12, 15 **5.** _____

6. Find x in $\triangle DEF$.
F 6 **H** $6\sqrt{3}$
G $6\sqrt{2}$ **J** 12 **6.** _____

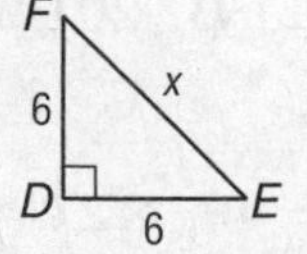

7. Find y in $\triangle XYZ$.
A $7.5\sqrt{3}$ **C** 15
B $15\sqrt{3}$ **D** 30 **7.** _____

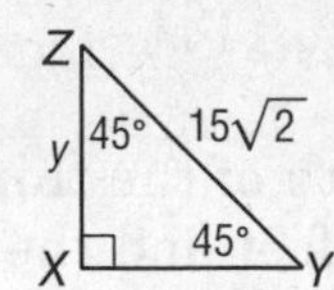

8. The length of the sides of a square is 10 meters. Find the length of the diagonals of the square.
F 10 m **H** $10\sqrt{3}$ m
G $10\sqrt{2}$ m **J** 20 m **8.** _____

9. Find x in $\triangle HJK$.
A $5\sqrt{2}$ **C** 10
B $5\sqrt{3}$ **D** 15 **9.** _____

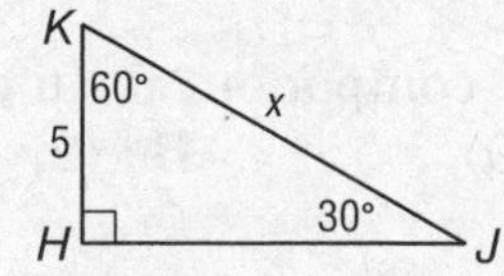

10. Find x in $\triangle ABC$.
F 25 **H** $25\sqrt{3}$
G $25\sqrt{2}$ **J** 100 **10.** _____

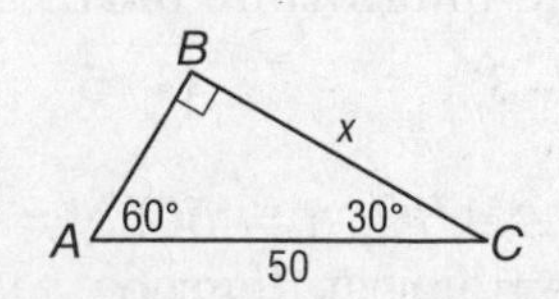

Assessment

NAME ______________________ DATE ____________ PERIOD ____________

8 Chapter 8 Test, Form 1 *(continued)*

11. Find x to the nearest tenth.

A 7.3 **C** 18.4

B 17.3 **D** 47.1

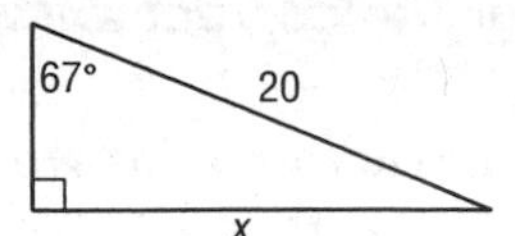

11. ______

12. Find the measure of the angle of elevation of the Sun when a pole 25 feet tall casts a shadow 42 feet long.

F 30.8° **G** 36.5° **H** 53.5° **J** 59.2°

12. ______

13. Which is the angle of depression in the figure at the right?

A $\angle AOT$ **C** $\angle TOB$

B $\angle AOB$ **D** $\angle BTO$

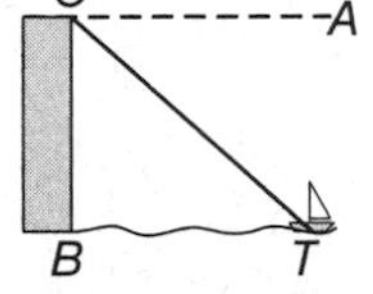

13. ______

14. Find y in $\triangle XYZ$ if $m\angle Y = 36$, $m\angle X = 49$, and $x = 12$. Round to the nearest hundredth.

F 0.04 **G** 9.35 **H** 14.80 **J** 15.41

14. ______

15. To find the distance between two points, A and B, on opposite sides of a river, a surveyor measures the distance from A to C as 200 feet, $m\angle A = 72$, and $m\angle B = 37$. Find the distance from A to B. Round your answer to the nearest tenth.

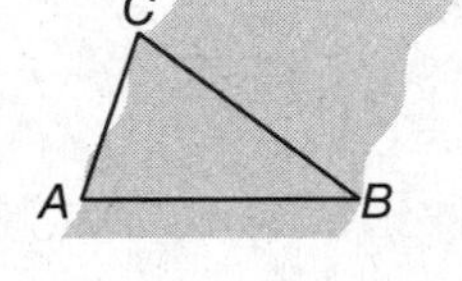

A 77.4 ft **B** 201.2 ft **C** 250.4 ft **D** 314.2 ft

15. ______

16. In $\triangle ABC$, $m\angle A = 40$, $m\angle C = 115$, and $b = 8$. Find a to the nearest tenth.

F 12.2 **G** 11.3 **H** 5.7 **J** 5.3

16. ______

17. Find the length of the third side of a triangular garden if two sides measure 8 feet and 12 feet and the included angle measures 50.

A 7.8 ft **B** 9.2 ft **C** 14.4 ft **D** 146.3 ft

17. ______

18. In $\triangle DEF$, $d = 20$, $e = 25$, and $f = 30$. Find $m\angle F$ to the nearest degree.

F 83° **G** 76° **H** 56° **J** 47°

18. ______

19. Find the component form of $\overrightarrow{AB}$ with $A(2, 3)$ and $B(-4, 6)$.

A $\langle -2, 9 \rangle$ **B** $\langle 2, -9 \rangle$ **C** $\langle -6, 3 \rangle$ **D** $\langle 6, -3 \rangle$

19. ______

20. Find the magnitude of $\overrightarrow{AB}$ with $A(3, 4)$ and $B(-1, 7)$.

F $\langle 4, -3 \rangle$ **G** 5 **H** $\sqrt{13}$ **J** 25

20. ______

Bonus In $\triangle ABC$, $a = 50$, $b = 48$, and $c = 40$. Find $m\angle A$ to the nearest degree.

B: ______________

NAME ______________________ DATE ____________ PERIOD ____________

8 Chapter 8 Test, Form 2A

SCORE ______

Write the letter for the correct answer in the blank at the right of each question.

1. Find the geometric mean between 7 and 12.

A 5 **C** $\sqrt{19}$

B 9.5 **D** $2\sqrt{21}$ **1.** ______

2. In $\triangle PQR$, $RS = 4$ and $QS = 6$. Find PS.

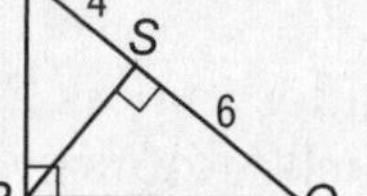

F 2 **H** $\sqrt{10}$

G 5 **J** $2\sqrt{6}$ **2.** ______

3. Find x.

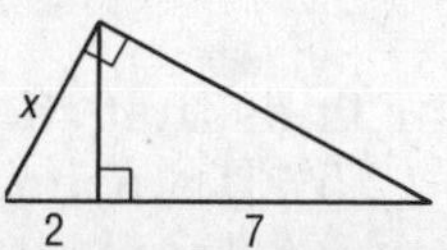

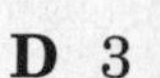

A $3\sqrt{2}$ **C** 4.5

B $\sqrt{14}$ **D** 3 **3.** ______

4. Find y.

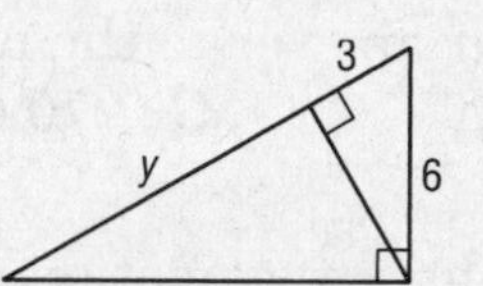

F 12 **H** 9

G 11 **J** 2 **4.** ______

5. Find the length of the hypotenuse of a right triangle with legs that measure 5 and 7.

A 12 **C** $\sqrt{35}$

B $\sqrt{24}$ **D** $\sqrt{74}$ **5.** ______

6. Find x.

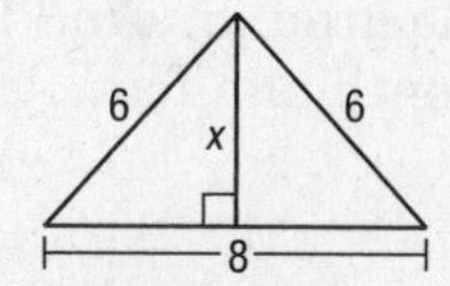

F 3 **H** $4\sqrt{3}$

G 4 **J** $2\sqrt{5}$ **6.** ______

7. Which set of measures could represent the lengths of the sides of a right triangle?

A 9, 40, 41 **C** 7, 8, 15

B 8, 30, 31 **D** $\sqrt{2}, \sqrt{3}, \sqrt{6}$ **7.** ______

8. Find c.

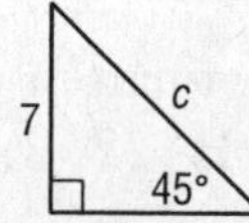

F 7 **H** $7\sqrt{3}$

G $7\sqrt{2}$ **J** 14 **8.** ______

9. Find the perimeter of a square if the length of its diagonal is 12 inches. Round to the nearest tenth.

A 8.5 in. **C** 48 in.

B 33.9 in. **D** 67.9 in. **9.** ______

10. Find x.

F 4 **H** $4\sqrt{3}$

G $4\sqrt{2}$ **J** $8\sqrt{3}$ **10.** ______

Assessment

NAME ______________________ DATE __________ PERIOD __________

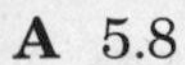

8 Chapter 8 Test, Form 2A *(continued)*

11. Find x to the nearest tenth.

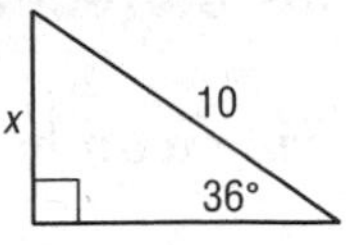

A 5.8 **C** 8.1

B 5.9 **D** 17.3

11. ______

12. Find x to the nearest degree.

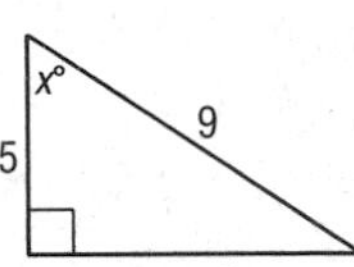

F 56 **H** 34

G 45 **J** 29

12. ______

13. If a 20-foot ladder makes a 65° angle with the ground, how many feet up a wall will it reach? Round your answer to the nearest tenth.

A 8.5 ft **B** 10 ft **C** 18.1 ft **D** 42.9 ft

13. ______

14. A ship's sonar finds that the angle of depression to a wreck on the bottom of the ocean is 12.5°. If a point on the ocean floor is 60 meters directly below the ship, how many meters is it from that point on the ocean floor to the wreck? Round your answer to the nearest tenth.

F 277.2 m **G** 270.6 m **H** 61.5 m **J** 13.3 m

14. ______

15. Find the angle of elevation of the sun if a building 100 feet tall casts a shadow 150 feet long. Round to the nearest degree.

A 60° **B** 48° **C** 42° **D** 34°

15. ______

16. When the Sun's angle of elevation is 73°, a tree tilted at an angle of 5° from the vertical casts a 20-foot shadow on the ground. Find the length of the tree to the nearest tenth of a foot.

5°
73°
20-foot shadow

F 6.3 ft **H** 51.1 ft

G 19.2 ft **J** 219.4 ft

16. ______

17. In $\triangle CDE$, $m\angle C = 52$, $m\angle D = 17$, and $e = 28.6$. Find c to the nearest tenth.

A 77.1 **B** 49.1 **C** 24.1 **D** 18.4

17. ______

18. In $\triangle PQR$, $p = 56$, $r = 17$, and $m\angle Q = 110$. Find q to the nearest tenth.

F 4076.2 **G** 63.8 **H** 52.6 **J** 3.1

18. ______

19. Find the component form of $\overrightarrow{CD}$ with $C(5, -7)$ and $D(-3, 9)$.

A $\langle -2, 2 \rangle$ **B** $\langle 2, 2 \rangle$ **C** $\langle 8, -16 \rangle$ **D** $\langle -8, 16 \rangle$

19. ______

20. A pilot is flying due east at a speed of 300 miles per hour and wind is blowing due north at 50 miles per hour. What is the magnitude of the resultant velocity of the plane?

F 300 mph **G** 350 mph **H** about 304 mph **J** 2500 mph

20. ______

Bonus From a window 20 feet above the ground, the angle of elevation to the top of another building is 35°. The distance between the buildings is 52 feet. Find the height of the building to the nearest tenth of a foot.

B: ______________

8 Chapter 8 Test, Form 2B

SCORE ________

Write the letter for the correct answer in the blank at the right of each question.

1. Find the geometric mean between 9 and 11.

A $3\sqrt{11}$ **C** 10

B $2\sqrt{5}$ **D** 2

1. ________

2. In $\triangle PQR$, $RS = 5$ and $QS = 8$. Find PS.

F 3 **H** $\sqrt{13}$

G 6.5 **J** $2\sqrt{10}$

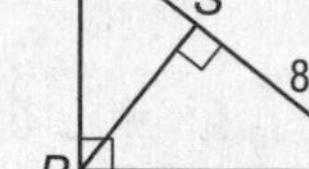

2. ________

3. Find x.

A 5.5 **C** $\sqrt{24}$

B $\sqrt{11}$ **D** $\sqrt{33}$

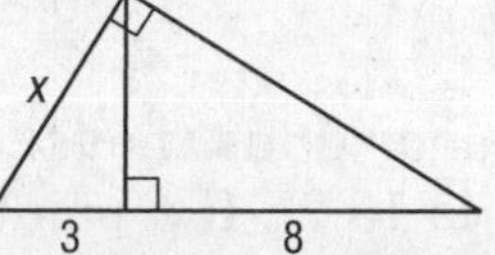

3. ________

4. Find y.

F 4 **H** 8

G 5 **J** 9

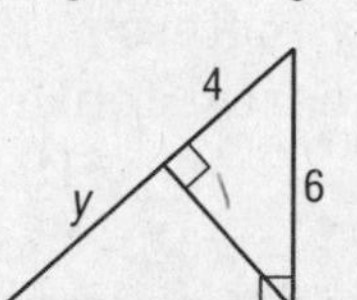

4. ________

5. Find the length of the hypotenuse of a right triangle whose legs measure 6 and 5.

A 11 **C** $\sqrt{30}$

B $\sqrt{11}$ **D** $\sqrt{61}$

5. ________

6. Find x.

F $\sqrt{39}$ **H** $5\sqrt{3}$

G 6 **J** 5

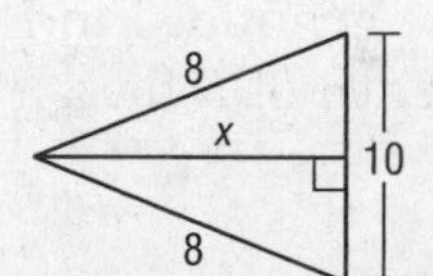

6. ________

7. Which set of measures could represent the lengths of the sides of a right triangle?

A $\frac{3}{4}, 1, \frac{5}{4}$ **C** 7, 17, 24

B $\sqrt{3}, \sqrt{5}, \sqrt{15}$ **D** 8, 15, 16

7. ________

8. Find c.

F 18 **H** $9\sqrt{2}$

G $9\sqrt{3}$ **J** 9

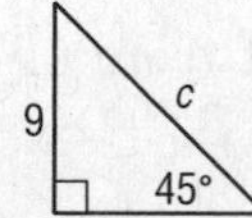

8. ________

9. Find the perimeter of a square if the length of its diagonal is 16 millimeters. Round to the nearest tenth.

A 11.3 mm **C** 90.5 mm

B 45.3 mm **D** 128.0 mm

9. ________

10. Find x.

F 6 **H** $6\sqrt{3}$

G $6\sqrt{2}$ **J** $12\sqrt{3}$

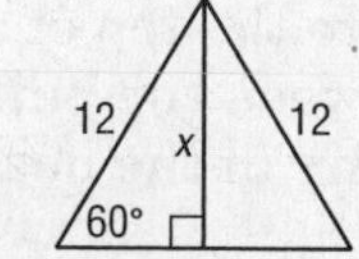

10. ________

Assessment

NAME ______________________ DATE ____________ PERIOD ____________

8 Chapter 8 Test, Form 2B *(continued)*

11. Find x.

A 8.0 **B** 8.9 **C** 10.4 **D** 10.8

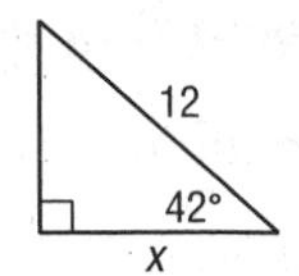

11. ____

12. Find x to the nearest degree.

F 57 **G** 55 **H** 33 **J** 29

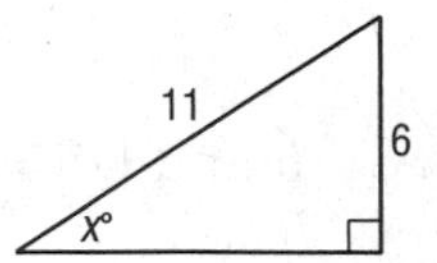

12. ____

13. If a 24-foot ladder makes a 58° angle with the ground, how many feet up a wall will it reach? Round your answer to the nearest tenth.

A 38.4 ft **B** 20.8 ft **C** 20.4 ft **D** 12.7 ft **13.** ____

14. A ship's sonar finds that the angle of depression to a wreck on the bottom of the ocean is 13.2°. If a point on the ocean floor is 75 meters directly below the ship, how many meters is it from that point on the ocean floor to the wreck? Round to the nearest tenth.

F 328.4 m **G** 319.8 m **H** 77.0 m **J** 17.6 m **14.** ____

15. Find the angle of elevation of the sun if a building 125 feet tall casts a shadow 196 feet long. Round to the nearest degree.

A 64° **B** 50° **C** 40° **D** 33° **15.** ____

16. When the sun's angle of elevation is 76°, a tree tilted at an angle of 4° from the vertical casts an 18-foot shadow on the ground. Find the length of the tree to the nearest tenth of a foot.

F 250.4 ft **G** 56.5 ft **H** 17.7 ft **J** 4.6 ft

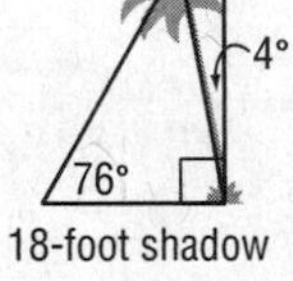

16. ____

17. In $\triangle ABC$, $m\angle A = 46$, $m\angle B = 105$, and $c = 19.8$. Find a to the nearest tenth.

A 29.4 **B** 28.5 **C** 15.7 **D** 14.7 **17.** ____

18. In $\triangle LMN$, $\ell = 42$, $m = 61$, and $m\angle N = 108$. Find n to the nearest tenth.

F 7068.4 **G** 84.1 **H** 79.2 **J** 24.7 **18.** ____

19. Find the component from of $\overrightarrow{EF}$ with $E(-11,-3)$ and $F(7,-4)$

A $\langle -18, 1\rangle$ **B** $\langle 18, -1\rangle$ **C** $\langle -4, -7\rangle$ **D** $\langle 4, 7\rangle$ **19.** ____

20. An eagle is traveling along a path due east at a rate of 50 miles per hour and the wind is blowing due north at 15 miles per hour. What is the magnitude of the resultant velocity of the eagle?

F 35 mph **G** 50 mph **H** 65 mph **J** about 52.2 mph **20.** ____

Bonus From a window 24 feet above the ground, the angle of elevation to the top of another building is 38°. The distance between the buildings is 63 feet. Find the height of the building to the nearest tenth of a foot.

B: ____________

NAME ________________________ DATE __________ PERIOD __________

8 Chapter 8 Test, Form 2C

SCORE ______

1. Find the geometric mean between 2 and 5. **1.** ____________

For Questions 2–5, find x.

2.

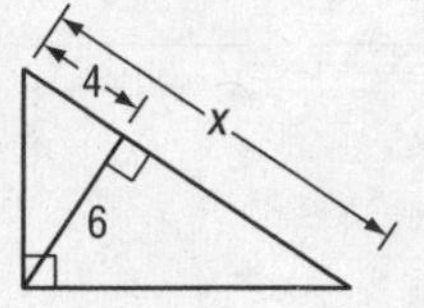

3.

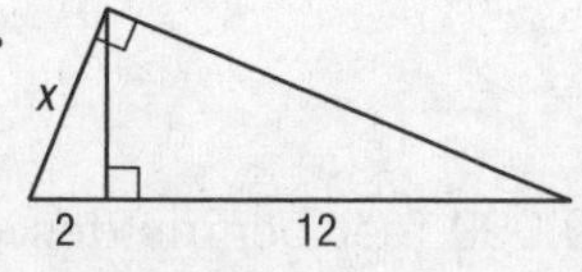

2. 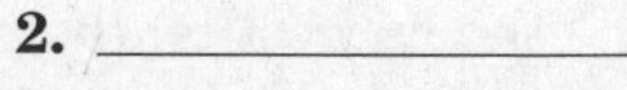

3. 

4. 60, x, 20

5. 20, 20, x, 20

4. 

5. 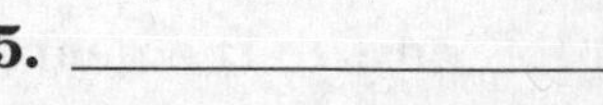

6. Find x.

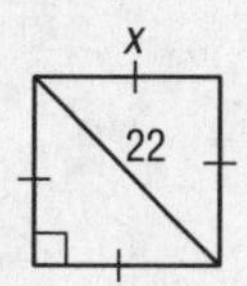

6. ____________

7. In parallelogram $ABCD$, $AD = 4$ and $m\angle D = 60$. Find AF.

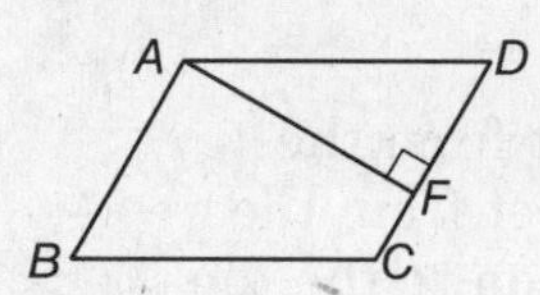

7. ____________

8. Find x and y.

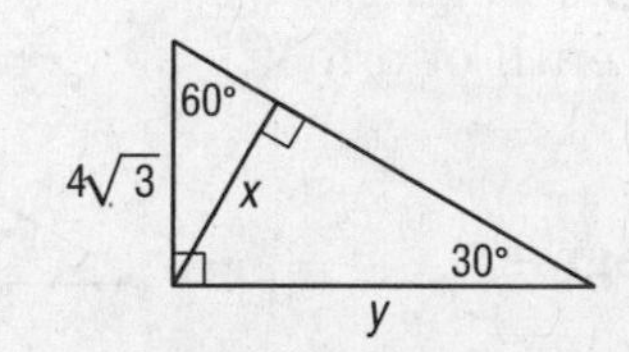

8. ____________

9. Find x to the nearest tenth.

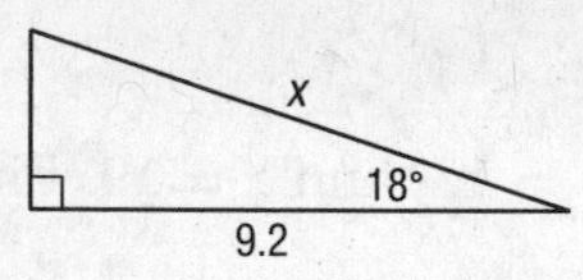

9. ____________

10. An A-frame house is 40 feet high and 30 feet wide. Find the measure of the angle that the roof makes with the floor. Round to the nearest degree.

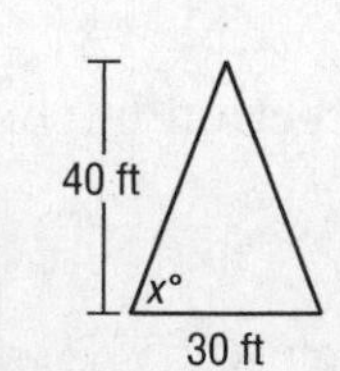

10. ____________

11. A 30-foot tree casts a 12-foot shadow. Find the measure of the angle of elevation of the Sun to the nearest degree. **11.** ____________

Assessment

NAME ____________________ DATE ____________ PERIOD ____________

8 Chapter 8 Test, Form 2C *(continued)*

12. A boat is 1000 meters from a cliff. If the angle of depression from the top of the cliff to the boat is 15°, how tall is the cliff? Round your answer to the nearest tenth.

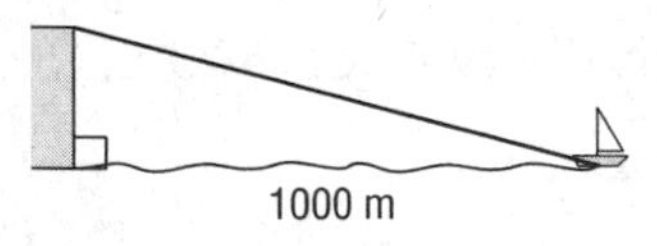

12. ____________

13. A plane flying at an altitude of 10,000 feet begins descending when the end of the runway is 50,000 feet from a point on the ground directly below the plane. Find the measure of the angle of descent (depression) to the nearest degree.

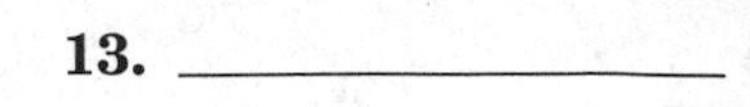

13. ____________

14. ____________

14. Find x to the nearest tenth.

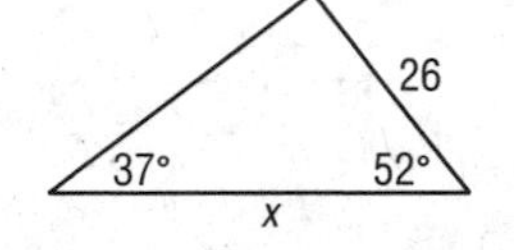

15. ____________

15. Find x to the nearest tenth.

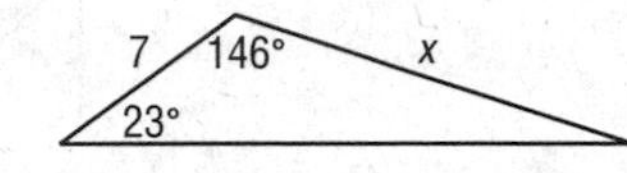

16. A tree grew at a 3° slant from the vertical. At a point 50 feet from the tree, the angle of elevation to the top of the tree is 17°. Find the height of the tree to the nearest tenth of a foot.

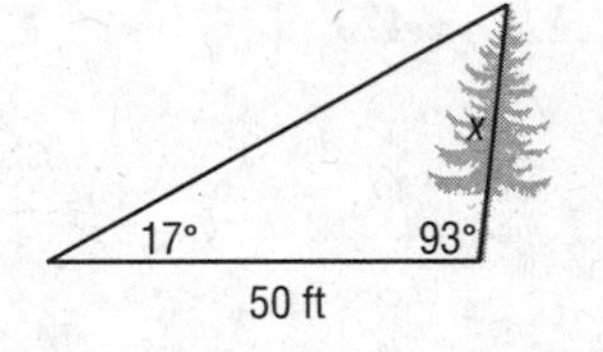

16. ____________

17. ____________

17. Find x to the nearest degree.

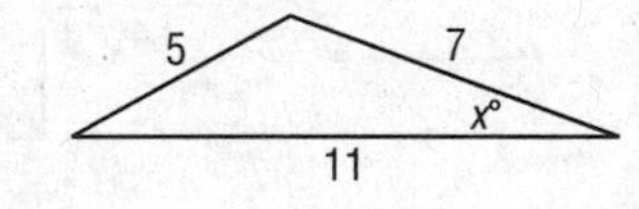

18. In $\triangle XYZ$, $m\angle X = 152$, $y = 15$, and $z = 19$. Find x to the nearest tenth.

18. ____________

19. Find the magnitude and direction of the vector $\overrightarrow{AZ}$: $A(8, 8)$ and $Z(1, -3)$.

19. ____________

20. Copy the vectors to find $\overrightarrow{s} + \overrightarrow{t}$.

20. ____________

B: ____________

Bonus Find x.

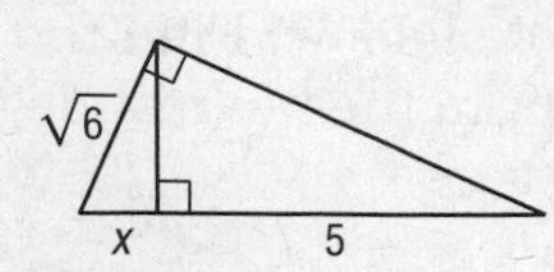

8 Chapter 8 Test, Form 2D

SCORE ________

1. Find the geometric mean between $3\sqrt{6}$ and $5\sqrt{6}$. **1.** ________

For Questions 2–5, find *x*.

2.

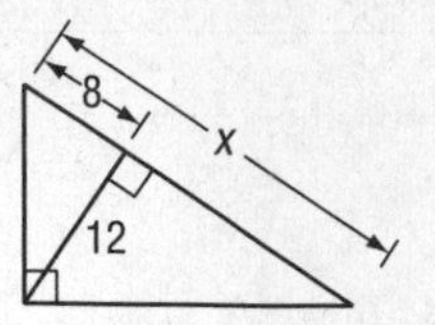

3.

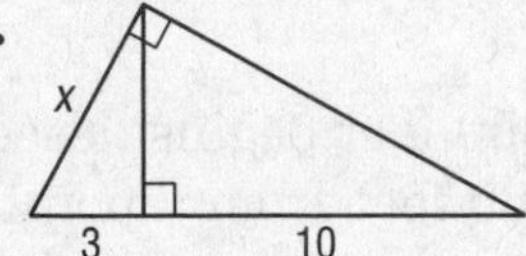

2. ________

3. ________

4.

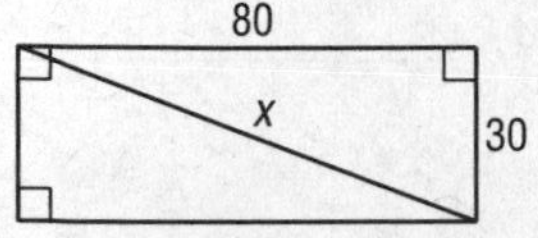

5.

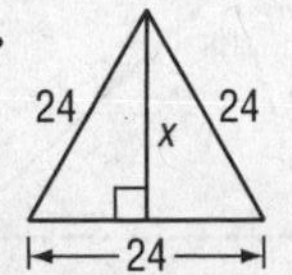

4. ________

5. ________

6. Find *x*.

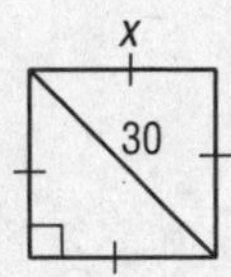

6. ________

7. In parallelogram $ABCD$, $AD = 14$ and $m\angle D = 60$. Find AF.

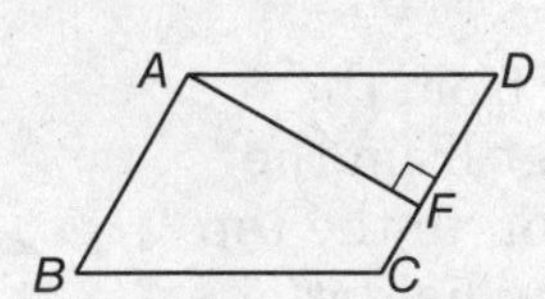

7. ________

8. Find x and y.

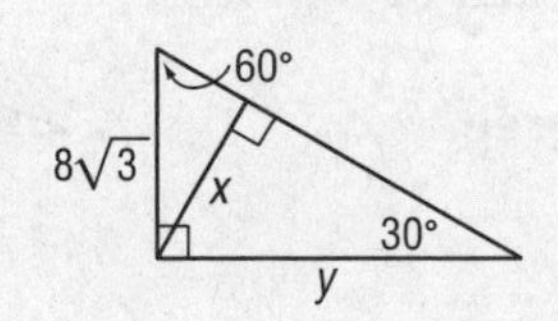

8. ________

9. Find x to the nearest tenth.

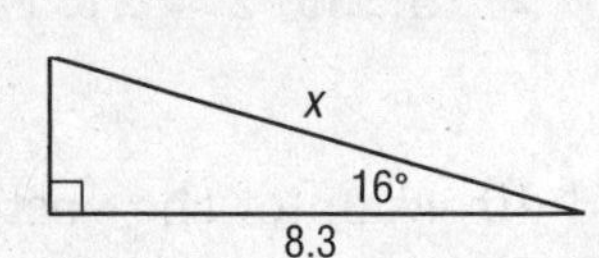

9. ________

10. An A-frame house is 45 feet high and 32 feet wide. Find the measure of the angle that the roof makes with the floor. Round to the nearest degree.

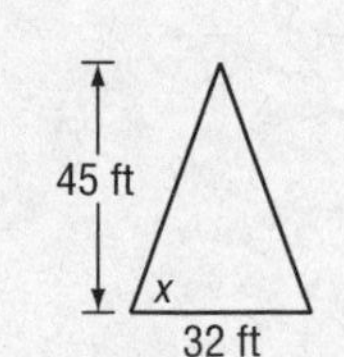

10. ________

11. A 38-foot tree casts a 16-foot shadow. Find the measure of the angle of elevation of the sun to the nearest degree. **11.** ________

Assessment

NAME ______________________ DATE ____________ PERIOD ____________

8 Chapter 8 Test, Form 2D *(continued)*

12. A boat is 2000 meters from a cliff. If the angle of depression from the top of the cliff to the boat is 10°, how tall is the cliff? Round your answer to the nearest tenth.

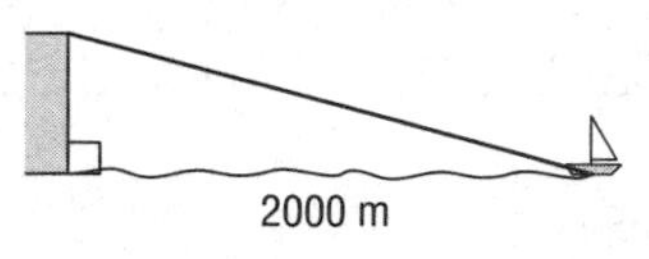

12. ____________

13. A plane flying at an altitude of 10,000 feet begins descending when the end of the runway is 60,000 feet from a point on the ground directly below the plane. Find the measure of the angle of descent (depression) to the nearest degree.

13. ____________

14. Find x to the nearest tenth.

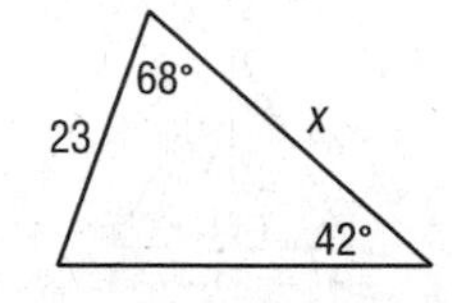

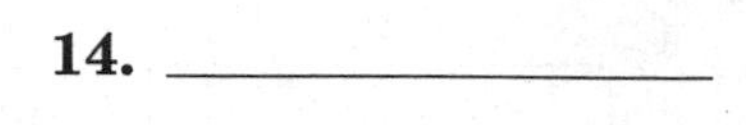

14. ____________

15. Find x to the nearest degree.

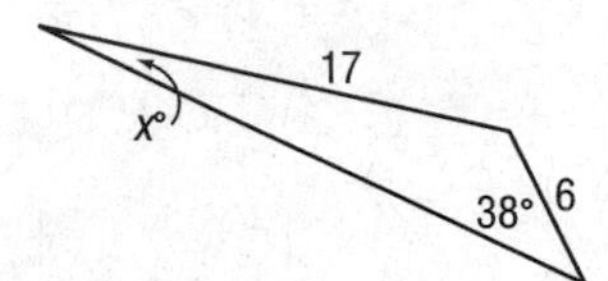

15. ____________

16. A tree grew at a 3° slant from the vertical. At a point 60 feet from the tree, the angle of elevation to the top of the tree is 14°. Find the height of the tree to the nearest tenth of a foot.

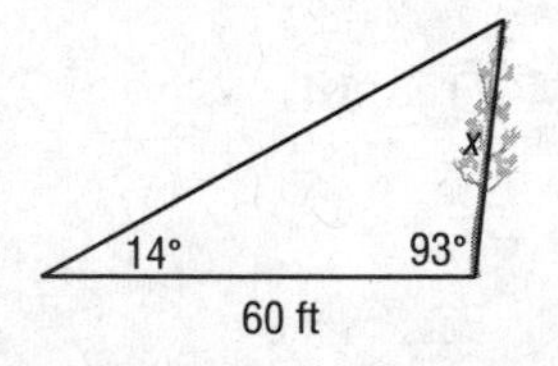

16. ____________

17. Find x to the nearest degree.

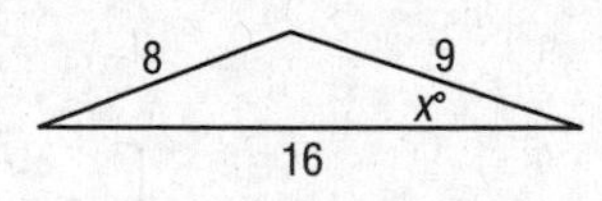

17. ____________

18. In $\triangle XYZ$, $m\angle X = 156$, $y = 18$, and $z = 21$. Find x to the nearest tenth.

18. ____________

19. Find the magnitude and direction of the vector $\overrightarrow{PQ}$: $P(-2, 4)$ and $Q(-5, -6)$.

19. ____________

20. Copy the vectors to find $\vec{d} - \vec{f}$.

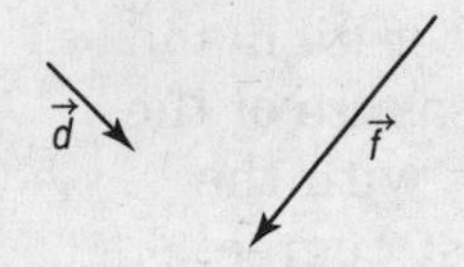

20. ____________

Bonus Find x.

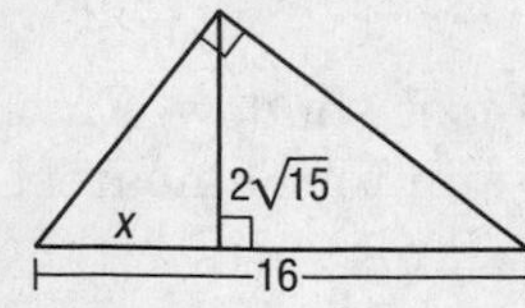

B: ____________

NAME ______________________ DATE ____________ PERIOD ____________

8 Chapter 8 Test, Form 3

SCORE ________

Assessment

1. Find the geometric mean between $\frac{2}{9}$ and $\frac{3}{9}$. **1.** ________

2. Find x in $\triangle PQR$. **2.** ________

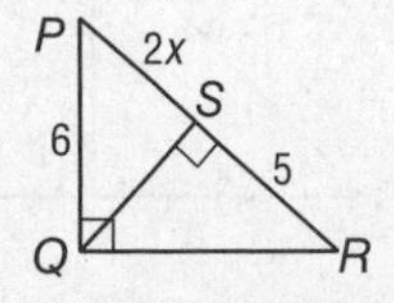

3. Find x in $\triangle XYZ$. **3.** ________

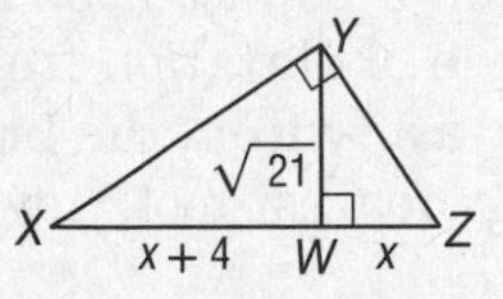

4. If the length of one leg of a right triangle is three times the length of the other and the hypotenuse is 20, find the length of the shorter leg. **4.** ________

5. Find the measure of the altitude drawn to the hypotenuse of a right triangle with legs that measure 3 and 4. **5.** ________

6. Find x. **6.** ________

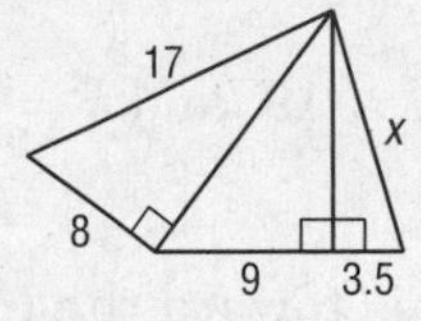

7. Richmond is 200 kilometers due east of Teratown and Hamilton is 150 kilometers directly north of Teratown. Find the shortest distance in kilometers between Hamilton and Richmond. **7.** ________

8. The measures of the sides of a triangle are 48, 55, and 73. Use the Pythagorean Theorem to classify the triangle as *acute*, *obtuse*, or *right*. **8.** ________

9. Find the exact perimeter of this square. **9.** ________

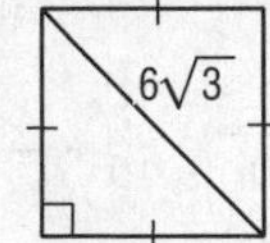

10. Find the exact perimeter of rectangle $ABCD$. **10.** ________

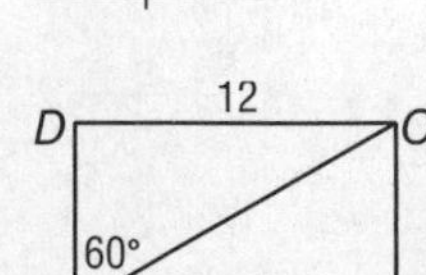

11. Find x and y. **11.** ________

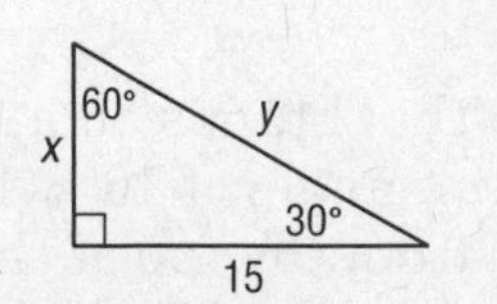

12. $\triangle ABC$ is a 30°-60°-90° triangle with right angle A and with $\overline{AC}$ as the longer leg. If $A(-4, -2)$ and $B(-4, 6)$, find the coordinates of C. **12.** ________

8 Chapter 8 Test, Form 3 *(continued)*

13. If $\overline{AB} \parallel \overline{CD}$, find x and the exact length of $\overline{CD}$.

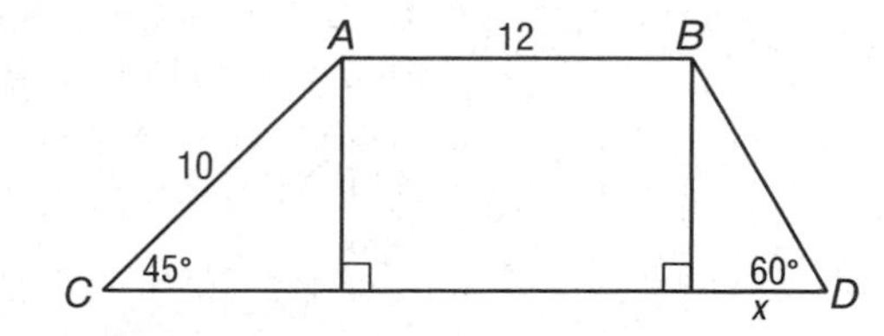

13. ____________

14. The angle of elevation from a point on the street to the top of a building is 29°. The angle of elevation from another point on the street, 50 feet farther away from the building, to the top of the building is 25°. To the nearest foot, how tall is the building?

14. ____________

15. The angle of depression from the top of a flagpole on top of a lighthouse to a boat on the ocean is 2.9°. The angle of depression from the bottom of the flagpole to the boat is 2.6°. If the boat is 400 feet away from shore and the lighthouse is right on the edge of the shore, how tall is the flagpole? Round your answer to the nearest foot.

15. ____________

16. In $\triangle JKL$, $m\angle J = 26.8$, $m\angle K = 19$, and $k = 17$. Find ℓ to the nearest tenth.

16. ____________

17. Don hit a golf ball from the tee toward the hole which is 250 yards away. However, due to the wind, his drive was 5° off course. If the angle between the segment from the hole to the tee and the segment from the hole to the ball measures 97°, how far did Don drive the ball? Round to the nearest tenth of a yard.

17. ____________

18. In $\triangle HJK$, $h = 7$, $j = 12.3$, and $k = 7.9$. Find $m\angle K$. Round your answer to the nearest degree.

18. ____________

19. Find the magnitude and direction of the vector $\overrightarrow{WZ}$: $W(15, 25)$ and $Z(10, -6)$.

19. ____________

20. Copy the vectors to find $\vec{a} + \vec{b}$ and $\vec{a} - \vec{b}$.

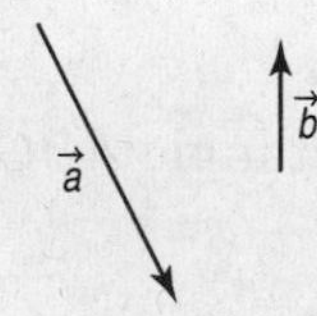

20. ____________

Bonus A 50-foot vertical pole that stands on a hillside. The slope of the hill side makes an angle of 10° with the horizontal. Two guy wires extend from the top of the pole to points on the hill 60 feet uphill and downhill from its base. Find the length of each guy wire to the nearest tenth of a foot.

B: ____________

NAME ______________________ DATE ____________ PERIOD ____________

8 Chapter 8 Extended-Response Test

SCORE ________

Demonstrate your knowledge by giving a clear, concise solution to each problem. Be sure to include all relevant drawings and justify your answers. You may show your solution in more than one way or investigate beyond the requirements of the problem.

1. If the geometric mean between 10 and x is 6, what is x? Show how you obtained your answer.

2.

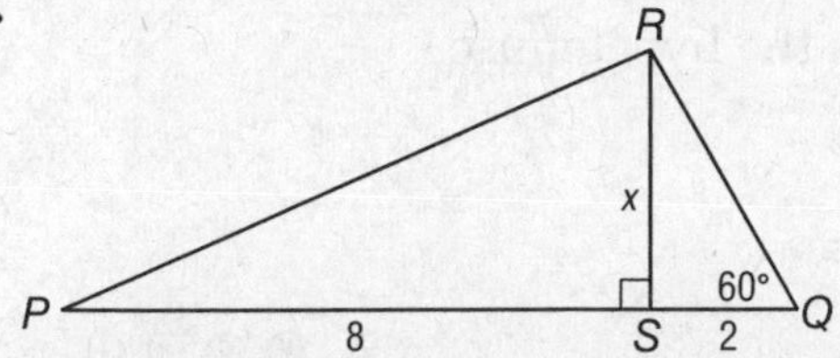

a. Max used the following equations to find x in $\triangle PQR$. Is Max correct? Explain.

$x = \sqrt{8 \cdot 2}$

$x = \sqrt{16}$

$x = 4$

b. If $\angle PRQ$ is a right angle, what is the measure of $\overline{PS}$?

c. Is $\triangle PRS$ a 45°-45°-90° triangle? Explain.

3. To solve for x in a triangle, when would you use *sin* and when would you use sin^{-1}? Give an example for each type of situation.

4. Draw a diagram showing the angles of elevation and depression and label each. How are the measures of these angles related?

5. Draw an obtuse triangle and label the vertices, the measures of two angles, and the length of one side. Explain how to solve the triangle.

6. Irina is solving $\triangle ABC$. She plans to first use the Law of Sines to find two of the angles. Is Irina's plan a good one? Explain.

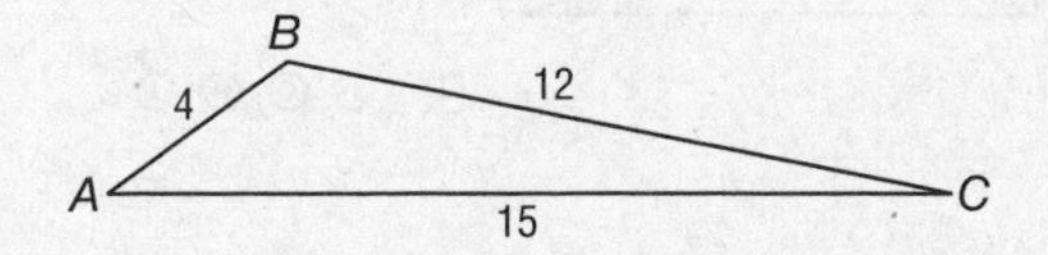

Assessment

NAME _______________ DATE _______ PERIOD _______

8 Standardized Test Practice

SCORE _______

(Chapters 1–8)

Part 1: Multiple Choice

Instructions: Fill in the appropriate circle for the best answer.

1. If $\overline{TA}$ bisects $\angle YTB$, $\overline{TC}$ bisects $\angle BTZ$, $m\angle YTA = 4y + 6$, and $m\angle BTC = 7y - 4$, find $m\angle CTZ$. (Lesson 1-4)

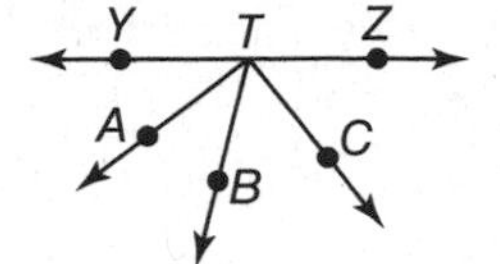

A 52 **B** 38 **C** 25 **D** 8

1. Ⓐ Ⓑ Ⓒ Ⓓ

2. Which statement is *always* true? (Lesson 2-5)

F If right triangle QPR has sides q, p, and r, where r is the hypotenuse, then $r^2 = p^2 + q^2$.

G If $\overline{EF} \parallel \overline{HJ}$, then $EF = HJ$.

H If $\overline{KL}$ and $\overline{VT}$ are cut by a transversal, then $\overline{KL} \parallel \overline{VT}$.

J If $\overline{DR}$ and $\overline{RH}$ are congruent, then R bisects $\overline{DH}$.

2. Ⓕ Ⓖ Ⓗ Ⓙ

3. The equation for $\overleftrightarrow{PT}$ is $y - 2 = 8(x + 3)$. Determine an equation for a line perpendicular to $\overleftrightarrow{PT}$. (Lesson 3-4)

A $y = \frac{1}{8}x - 7$ **B** $y = 8x - 13$ **C** $y = -\frac{1}{8}x + 2$ **D** $y = -8x$

3. Ⓐ Ⓑ Ⓒ Ⓓ

4. Angle Y in $\triangle XYZ$ measures 90°. $\overline{XY}$ and $\overline{YZ}$ each measure 16 meters. Classify $\triangle XYZ$. (Lesson 4-1)

F acute and isosceles

G equiangular and equilateral

H right and scalene

J right and isosceles

4. Ⓕ Ⓖ Ⓗ Ⓙ

5. Two sides of a triangle measure 4 inches and 9 inches. Determine which cannot be the perimeter of the triangle. (Lesson 5-3)

A 19 in. **B** 21 in. **C** 23 in. **D** 26 in.

5. Ⓐ Ⓑ Ⓒ Ⓓ

6. $\triangle ABC \sim \triangle STR$, so $\frac{AB}{CA} =$ ___?___. (Lesson 6-2)

F $\frac{AB}{BC}$ **G** $\frac{ST}{RS}$ **H** $\frac{TR}{RS}$ **J** $\frac{RS}{ST}$

6. Ⓕ Ⓖ Ⓗ Ⓙ

7. The Petronas Towers in Kuala Lumpur, Malaysia, are 452 meters tall. A woman who is 1.75 meters tall stands 120 meters from the base of one tower. Find the angle of elevation between the woman's hat and the top of the tower. Round to the nearest tenth. (Lesson 8-5)

A 14.8° **B** 34.9° **C** 55° **D** 75.1°

7. Ⓐ Ⓑ Ⓒ Ⓓ

8. Which equation can be used to find x? (Lesson 8-4)

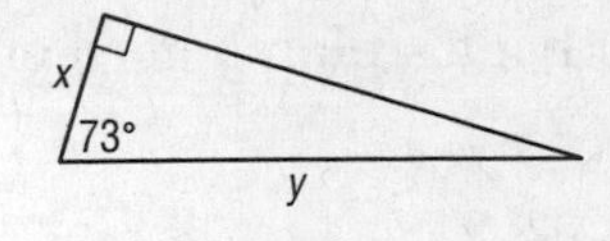

F $x = y \sin 73°$ **H** $x = \frac{y}{\cos 73°}$

G $x = y \cos 73°$ **J** $x = \frac{y}{\sin 73°}$

8. Ⓕ Ⓖ Ⓗ Ⓙ

9. Which inequality describes the possible values of x? (Lesson 5-6)

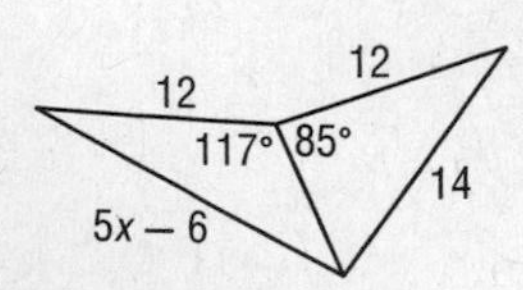

A $x < 4$ **C** $x > 2$

B $x < 2$ **D** $x > 4$

9. Ⓐ Ⓑ Ⓒ Ⓓ

8 Standardized Test Practice *(continued)*

10. Ashley wants to make a poster for her campaign from a photograph. She uses a photocopier to enlarge the 4 inch by 6 inch photograph. What are the dimensions of the poster if she increases the size of the photograph by a scale factor of 5? (Lesson 7-7)

F 2000 inches by 3000 inches **H** 9 inches by 11 inches
G 0.8 inches by 1.2 inches **J** 20 inches by 30 inches

10. Ⓕ Ⓖ Ⓗ Ⓙ

11. Find x. (Lesson 6-2)

A -3 **C** 5
B 3 **D** 9

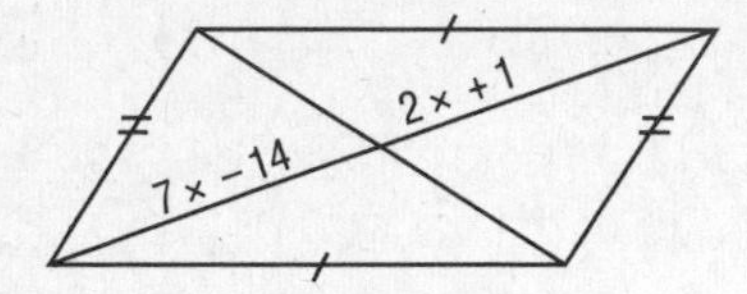

11. Ⓐ Ⓑ Ⓒ Ⓓ

12. Trapezoid $ABCD$ has vertices $A(1, 6)$, $B(-2, 6)$, $C(-10, -10)$, and $D(20, -10)$. Find the measure of $ABCD$'s midsegment to the nearest tenth. (Lesson 6-6)

F 3 **G** 5.3 **H** 7.2 **J** 16.5

12. Ⓕ Ⓖ Ⓗ Ⓙ

For Questions 13 and 14, use the figure to the right.

P 60° 10 30° L 9 Q 5 R M

13. Find QP to the nearest tenth. (Lesson 8-2)

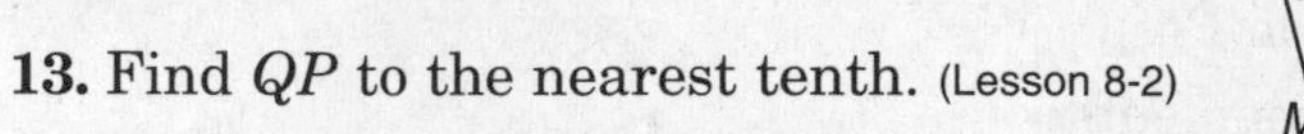

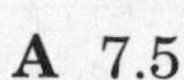

A 7.5 **B** 12 **C** 18.3 **D** 19.6

13. Ⓐ Ⓑ Ⓒ Ⓓ

14. Find LM. (Lesson 8-3)

F 5 **G** $5\sqrt{3}$ **H** 9 **J** $10\sqrt{3}$

14. Ⓕ Ⓖ Ⓗ Ⓙ

Part 2: Gridded Response

Instructions: Enter your answer by writing each digit of the answer in a column box and then shading in the appropriate circle that corresponds to that entry.

15. Find x so that $\ell \parallel m$. (Lesson 3-5)

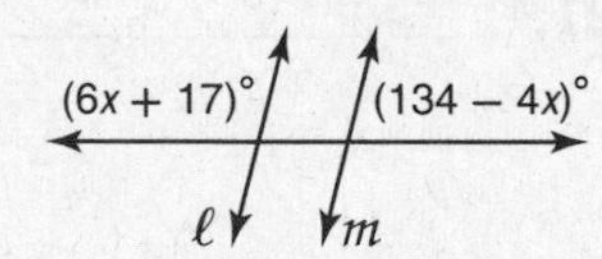

15.

16. Find c to the nearest tenth. (Lesson 8-6)

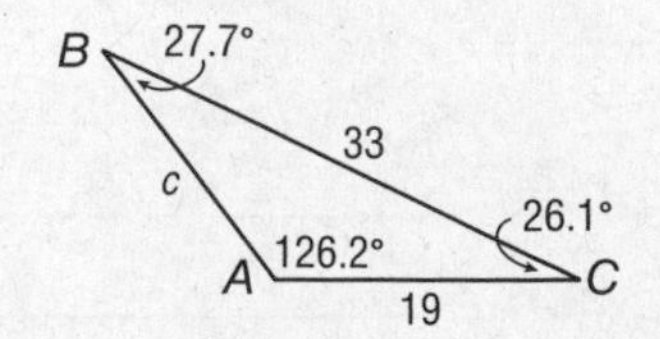

16.

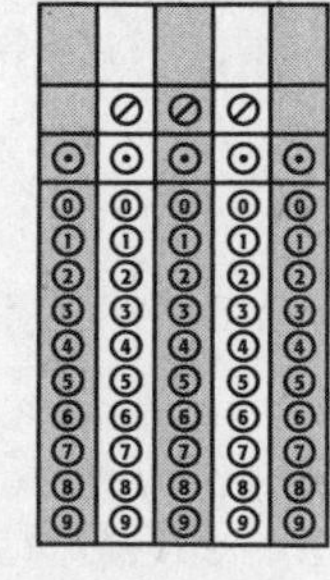

NAME ______________________ DATE ____________ PERIOD ____________

8 Standardized Test Practice *(continued)*

Part 3: Short Response

Instructions: Write your answer in the space provided.

For Questions 17 and 18, complete the following proof. (Lesson 2-7)

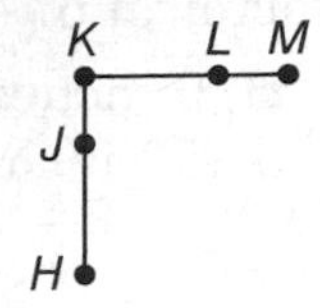

Given: $\overline{JK} \cong \overline{LM}$
$\overline{HJ} \cong \overline{KL}$

Prove: $\overline{HK} \cong \overline{KM}$

Proof:

Statements	Reasons
1. $\overline{JK} \cong \overline{LM}$, $\overline{HJ} \cong \overline{KL}$	**1.** Given
2. $JK = LM$, $HJ = KL$	**2.** (Question 17)
3. (Question 18)	**3.** Segment Addition Post.
4. $HJ + JK = KL + LM$	**4.** Add. Prop. of Equality
5. $HK = KM$	**5.** Substitution Prop.
6. $\overline{HK} \cong \overline{KM}$	**6.** Def. of $\cong$ segments

17. ____________

18. ____________

For Questions 19 and 20, use the figure at the right.

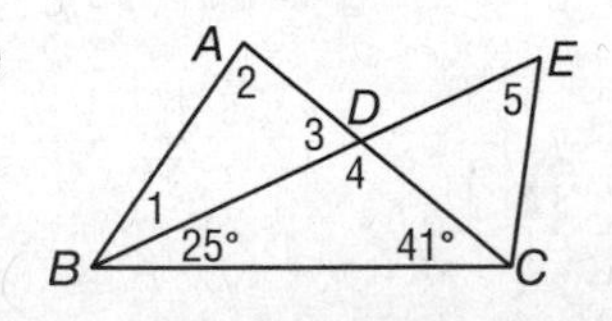

19. Find the measure of the numbered angles if $m\angle ABC = 57$ and $m\angle BCE = 98$. (Lesson 4-2)

19. ____________

20. If $\overline{BD}$ is a midsegment of $\triangle ABC$, $AD = 2x - 6$, and $DC = 22.5 - 4x$, find AC. (Lesson 5-2)

20. ____________

21. If $\triangle DEF \cong \triangle HJK$, $m\angle D = 26$, $m\angle J = 3x + 5$, and $m\angle F = 92$, find x. (Lesson 4-3)

21. ____________

22. Use the Exterior Angle Inequality Theorem to list all of the angles with measures that are less than $m\angle 1$. (Lesson 5-3)

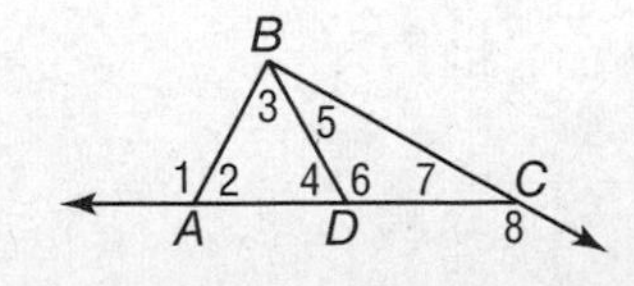

22. ____________

23. a. Determine whether $\triangle EFH \sim \triangle JGH$. Justify your answer. (Lesson 7-3)

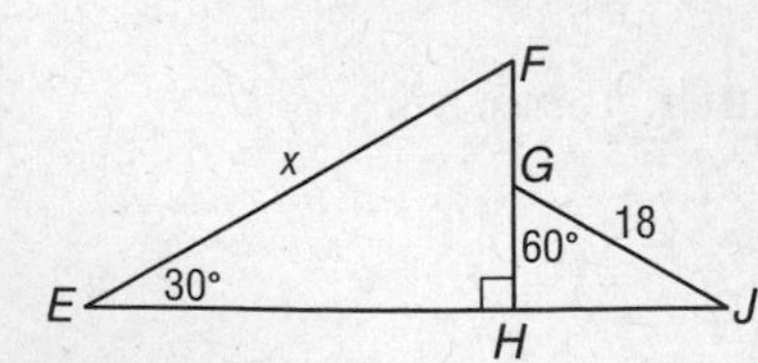

b. If G is the midpoint of $\overline{FH}$, find x. (Lesson 8-3)

c. Use the value of x you found in part **b** to find the scale factor of $\triangle EFH$ to $\triangle JGH$. (Lesson 7-3)

23a. ____________

23b. ____________

23c. ____________

NAME ________________ DATE ________ PERIOD ________

8 Anticipation Guide

Right Triangles and Trigonometry

Step 1 ***Before you begin Chapter 8***

- Read each statement.
- Decide whether you Agree (A) or Disagree (D) with the statement.
- Write A or D in the first column OR if you are not sure whether you agree or disagree, write NS (Not Sure).

STEP 1 A, D, or NS	Statement	STEP 2 A or D
	1. The geometric mean between two numbers is the positive square root of their product.	**A**
	2. An altitude drawn from the right angle of a right triangle to its hypotenuse separates the triangle into two congruent triangles.	**D**
	3. In a right triangle, the length of the hypotenuse is equal to the sum of the lengths of the legs.	**D**
	4. If any triangle has sides with lengths 3, 4, and 5, then that triangle is a right triangle.	**A**
	5. If the two acute angles of a right triangle are 45°, then the length of the hypotenuse is $\sqrt{2}$ times the length of either leg.	**A**
	6. In any triangle whose angle measures are 30°, 60°, and 90°, the hypotenuse is $\sqrt{3}$ times as long as the shorter leg.	**D**
	7. The sine ratio of an angle of a right triangle is equal to the length of the adjacent side divided by the length of the hypotenuse.	**D**
	8. The tangent of an angle of a right triangle whose sides have lengths 3, 4, and 5 will be smaller than the tangent of an angle of a right triangle whose sides have lengths 6, 8, and 10.	**D**
	9. Trigonometric ratios can be used to solve problems involving angles of elevation and angles of depression.	**A**
	10. The Law of Sines can only be used in right triangles.	**D**

Step 2 ***After you complete Chapter 8***

- Reread each statement and complete the last column by entering an A or a D.
- Did any of your opinions about the statements change from the first column?
- For those statements that you mark with a D, use a piece of paper to write an example of why you disagree.

NAME ________________ DATE ________ PERIOD ________

8-1 Study Guide and Intervention

Geometric Mean

Geometric Mean The **geometric mean** between two numbers is the positive square root of their product. For two positive numbers a and b, the geometric mean of a and b is the positive number x in the proportion $\frac{a}{x} = \frac{x}{b}$. Cross multiplying gives $x^2 = ab$, so $x = \sqrt{ab}$.

Example **Find the geometric mean between each pair of numbers.**

a. 12 and 3

$x = \sqrt{ab}$ — Definition of geometric mean

$= \sqrt{12 \cdot 3}$ — $a = 12$ and $b = 3$

$= \sqrt{(2 \cdot 2 \cdot 3) \cdot 3}$ — Factor.

$= 6$ — Simplify.

The geometric mean between 12 and 3 is 6.

b. 8 and 4

$x = \sqrt{ab}$ — Definition of geometric mean

$= \sqrt{8 \cdot 4}$ — $a = 8$ and $b = 4$

$= \sqrt{(2 \cdot 4) \cdot 4}$ — Factor.

$= \sqrt{16 \cdot 2}$ — Associative Property

$= 4\sqrt{2}$ — Simplify.

The geometric mean between 8 and 4 is $4\sqrt{2}$ or about 5.7.

Exercises

Find the geometric mean between each pair of numbers.

1. 4 and 4 **4**
2. 4 and 6 $\mathbf{\sqrt{24}}$ **or** $\mathbf{2\sqrt{6} \approx 4.9}$
3. 6 and 9 $\mathbf{\sqrt{54}}$ **or** $\mathbf{3\sqrt{6} \approx 7.3}$
4. $\frac{1}{2}$ and 2 **1**
5. 12 and 20 $\mathbf{\sqrt{240}}$ **or** $\mathbf{4\sqrt{15} \approx 15.5}$
6. 4 and 25 **10**
7. 16 and 30 $\mathbf{\sqrt{480}}$ **or** $\mathbf{4\sqrt{30} \approx 21.9}$
8. 10 and 100 $\mathbf{\sqrt{1000}}$ **or** $\mathbf{10\sqrt{10} \approx 31.6}$
9. $\frac{1}{2}$ and $\frac{1}{4}$ $\mathbf{\sqrt{\frac{1}{8}}}$ **or** $\mathbf{\frac{\sqrt{2}}{4} \approx 0.4}$
10. 17 and 3 $\mathbf{\sqrt{51} \approx 7.1}$
11. 4 and 16 **8**
12. 3 and 24 $\mathbf{\sqrt{72}}$ **or** $\mathbf{6\sqrt{2} \approx 8.5}$

NAME ______________________ DATE __________ PERIOD ________

8-1 Study Guide and Intervention *(continued)*

Geometric Mean

Geometric Means in Right Triangles In the diagram, $\triangle ABC \sim \triangle ADB \sim \triangle BDC$. An altitude to the hypotenuse of a right triangle forms two right triangles. The two triangles are similar and each is similar to the original triangle.

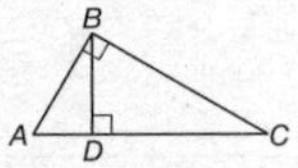

Example 1 **Use right $\triangle ABC$ with $\overline{BD} \perp \overline{AC}$. Describe two geometric means.**

a. $\triangle ADB \sim \triangle BDC$ so $\frac{AD}{BD} = \frac{BD}{CD}$.

In $\triangle ABC$, the altitude is the geometric mean between the two segments of the hypotenuse.

b. $\triangle ABC \sim \triangle ADB$ and $\triangle ABC \sim \triangle BDC$, so $\frac{AC}{AB} = \frac{AB}{AD}$ and $\frac{AC}{BC} = \frac{BC}{DC}$.

In $\triangle ABC$, each leg is the geometric mean between the hypotenuse and the segment of the hypotenuse adjacent to that leg.

Example 2 **Find x, y, and z.**

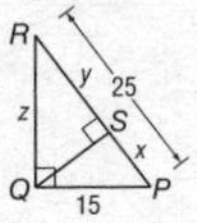

$15 = \sqrt{RP \cdot SP}$ Geometric Mean (Leg) Theorem

$15 = \sqrt{25x}$ $RP = 25$ and $SP = x$

$225 = 25x$ Square each side.

$9 = x$ Divide each side by 25.

Then

$y = RP - SP$

$= 25 - 9$

$= 16$

$z = \sqrt{RS \cdot RP}$ Geometric Mean (Leg) Theorem

$= \sqrt{16 \cdot 25}$ $RS = 16$ and $RP = 25$

$= \sqrt{400}$ Multiply.

$= 20$ Simplify.

Exercises

Find x, y, and z to the nearest tenth.

1. $x = \sqrt{3} \approx 1.7$

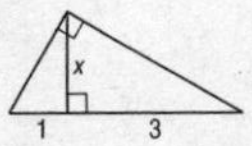

2. $x = \sqrt{10} \approx 3.2$; $y = \sqrt{14} \approx 3.7$; $z = \sqrt{35} \approx 5.9$

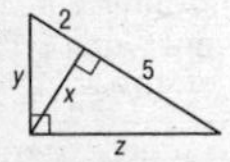

3. $x = 3$; $y = \sqrt{72}$ or $6\sqrt{2} \approx 8.5$; $z = \sqrt{8}$ or $2\sqrt{2} \approx 2.8$

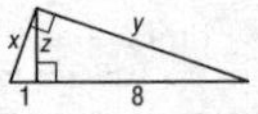

4. $x = 2$; $y = 3$

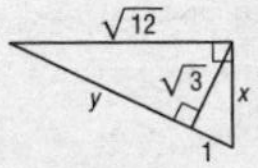

5. $x = 2$; $y = \sqrt{8}$ or $2\sqrt{2} \approx 2.8$; $z = \sqrt{8}$ or $2\sqrt{2} \approx 2.8$

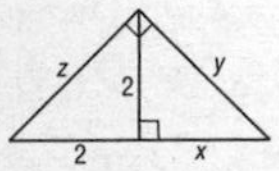

6. $x = \sqrt{12}$ or $2\sqrt{3} \approx 3.5$; $y = \sqrt{8}$ or $2\sqrt{2} \approx 2.8$; $z = \sqrt{24}$ or $2\sqrt{6} \approx 4.9$

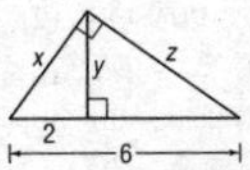

NAME ______________________ DATE __________ PERIOD ________

8-1 Skills Practice

Geometric Mean

Find the geometric mean between each pair of numbers.

1. 2 and 8 — **4**

2. 9 and 36 — **18**

3. 4 and 7 — $\sqrt{28}$ or $2\sqrt{7} \approx 5.3$

4. 5 and 10 — $\sqrt{50}$ or $5\sqrt{2} \approx 7.1$

5. 28 and 14 — $\sqrt{392}$ or $14\sqrt{2} \approx 19.8$

6. 7 and 36 — $\sqrt{252}$ or $6\sqrt{7} \approx 15.9$

Write a similarity statement identifying the three similar triangles in the figure.

7. $\triangle ACB \sim \triangle CDB \sim \triangle ADC$

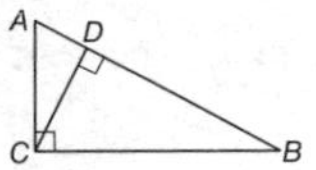

8. $\triangle MNL \sim \triangle NPL \sim \triangle MPN$

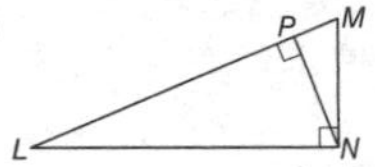

9. $\triangle EGF \sim \triangle GHF \sim \triangle EHG$

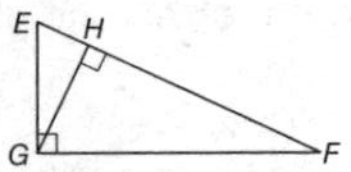

10. $\triangle RST \sim \triangle SUT \sim \triangle RUS$

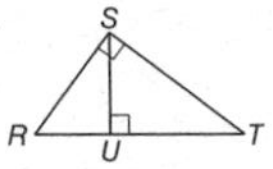

Find x, y and z.

11. 6; $\sqrt{108}$ or $6\sqrt{3} \approx 10.4$; $\sqrt{27}$ or $3\sqrt{3} \approx 5.2$

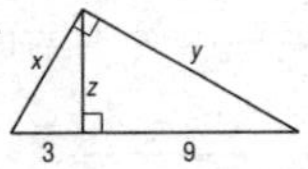

12. $\sqrt{40}$ or $2\sqrt{10} \approx 6.3$; $\sqrt{56}$ or $2\sqrt{14} \approx 7.5$; $\sqrt{140}$ or $2\sqrt{35} \approx 11.8$

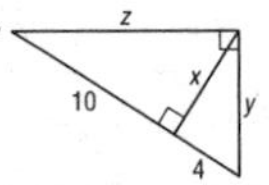

13. $\sqrt{60}$ or $2\sqrt{15} \approx 7.7$; $\sqrt{285}$ or $2\sqrt{19} \approx 16.9$; $\sqrt{76} \approx 8.7$

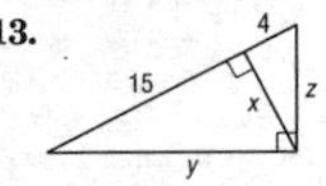

14. 12.5; $\sqrt{29} \approx 5.4$; $\sqrt{181.25} \approx 13.5$

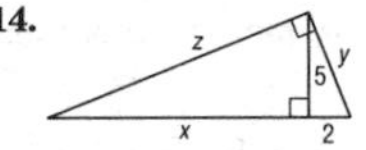

NAME ______________ DATE ________ PERIOD ________

8-1 Practice

Geometric Mean

Find the geometric mean between each pair of numbers.

1. 8 and 12
   $\sqrt{96}$ or $4\sqrt{6} \approx 9.8$

2. 3 and 15
   $\sqrt{45}$ or $3\sqrt{5} \approx 6.7$

3. $\frac{4}{5}$ and 2
   $\sqrt{\frac{8}{5}}$ or $\frac{2\sqrt{10}}{5} \approx 1.3$

Write a similarity statement identifying the three similar triangles in the figure.

4. **$\triangle VUT \sim \triangle UAT \sim \triangle VAU$**

5. **$\triangle JLK \sim \triangle LMK \sim \triangle JML$**

Find x, y, and z.

6. **$x = \sqrt{184}$ or $2\sqrt{46} \approx 13.6$;**
   $y = \sqrt{248}$ or $2\sqrt{62} \approx 15.7$
   $z = \sqrt{713} \approx 26.7$

7. **$x = \sqrt{114} \approx 10.7$;**
   $y = \sqrt{150}$ or $5\sqrt{6} \approx 12.2$
   $z = \sqrt{475}$ or $5\sqrt{19} \approx 21.8$

8. **$x = 4.5$;**
   $x = \sqrt{13} \approx 3.6$; 6.5

9. **$x = 15$;**
   $y = 5$;
   $z = \sqrt{300}$ or $10\sqrt{3} \approx 17.3$

10. **CIVIL** An airport, a factory, and a shopping center are at the vertices of a right triangle formed by three highways. The airport and factory are 6.0 miles apart. Their distances from the shopping center are 3.6 miles and 4.8 miles, respectively. A service road will be constructed from the shopping center to the highway that connects the airport and factory. What is the shortest possible length for the service road? Round to the nearest hundredth. **2.88 mi**

NAME ______________ DATE ________ PERIOD ________

8-1 Word Problem Practice

Geometric Mean

1. **SQUARES** Wilma has a rectangle of dimensions ℓ by w. She would like to replace it with a square that has the same area. What is the side length of the square with the same area as Wilma's rectangle?
   $\sqrt{\ell w}$, the geometric mean of ℓ and w

2. **EQUALITY** Gretchen computed the geometric mean of two numbers. One of the numbers was 7 and the geometric mean turned out to be 7 as well. What was the other number?
   7

3. **VIEWING ANGLE** A photographer wants to take a picture of a beach front. His camera has a viewing angle of 90° and he wants to make sure two palm trees located at points A and B in the figure are just inside the edges of the photograph.

   He walks out on a walkway that goes over the ocean to get the shot. If his camera has a viewing angle of 90°, at what distance down the walkway should he stop to take his photograph?
   60 ft

4. **EXHIBITIONS** A museum has a famous statue on display. The curator places the statue in the corner of a rectangular room and builds a 15-foot-long railing in front of the statue. Use the information below to find how close visitors will be able to get to the statue.
   7.2 ft

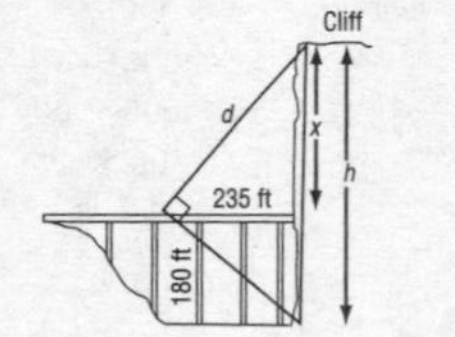

5. **CLIFFS** A bridge connects to a tunnel as shown in the figure. The bridge is 180 feet above the ground. At a distance of 235 feet along the bridge out of the tunnel, the angle to the base and summit of the cliff is a right angle.

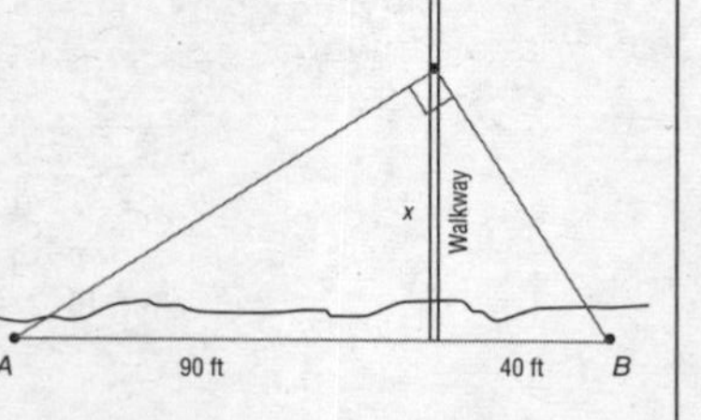

   a. What is the height of the cliff? Round to the nearest whole number.
   307 ft

   b. How high is the cliff from base to summit? Round to the nearest whole number.
   487 ft

   c. What is the value of d? Round to the nearest whole number.
   387 ft

Lesson 8-1

Answers

NAME ________________ DATE ________ PERIOD ________

8-1 Enrichment

Mathematics and Music

Pythagoras, a Greek philosopher who lived during the sixth century B.C., believed that all nature, beauty, and harmony could be expressed by whole-number relationships. Most people remember Pythagoras for his teachings about right triangles. (The sum of the squares of the legs equals the square of the hypotenuse.) But Pythagoras also discovered relationships between the musical notes of a scale. These relationships can be expressed as ratios.

C	D	E	F	G	A	B	C′
$\frac{1}{1}$	$\frac{8}{9}$	$\frac{4}{5}$	$\frac{3}{4}$	$\frac{2}{3}$	$\frac{3}{5}$	$\frac{8}{15}$	$\frac{1}{2}$

When you play a stringed instrument, you produce different notes by placing your finger on different places on a string. This is the result of changing the length of the vibrating part of the string.

The C string can be used to produce F by placing a finger $\frac{3}{4}$ of the way along the string.

Suppose a C string has a length of 16 inches. Write and solve proportions to determine what length of string would have to vibrate to produce the remaining notes of the scale.

1. D **$14\frac{2}{9}$ in.**
2. E **$12\frac{4}{5}$ in.**
3. F **12 in.**
4. G **$10\frac{2}{3}$ in.**
5. A **$9\frac{3}{5}$ in.**
6. B **$8\frac{8}{15}$ in.**
7. C′ **8 in.**

8. Complete to show the distance between finger positions on the 16-inch C string for each note. For example, $C(16) - D\left(14\frac{2}{9}\right) = 1\frac{7}{9}$.

C $1\frac{7}{9}$ in. D **$3\frac{1}{5}$ in.** E **4 in.** F **$5\frac{1}{3}$ in.** G **$6\frac{2}{5}$ in.** A **$7\frac{7}{15}$ in.** B **8 in.** C′

NAME ________________ DATE ________ PERIOD ________

8-2 Study Guide and Intervention

The Pythagorean Theorem and Its Converse

The Pythagorean Theorem In a right triangle, the sum of the squares of the lengths of the legs equals the square of the length of the hypotenuse. If the three whole numbers a, b, and c satisfy the equation $a^2 + b^2 = c^2$, then the numbers a, b, and c form a **Pythagorean triple.**

$\triangle ABC$ is a right triangle, so $a^2 + b^2 = c^2$.

Example

a. Find a.

$a^2 + b^2 = c^2$	Pythagorean Theorem
$a^2 + 12^2 = 13^2$	$b = 12, c = 13$
$a^2 + 144 = 169$	Simplify.
$a^2 = 25$	Subtract.
$a = 5$	Take the positive square root of each side.

b. Find c.

$a^2 + b^2 = c^2$	Pythagorean Theorem
$20^2 + 30^2 = c^2$	$a = 20, b = 30$
$400 + 900 = c^2$	Simplify.
$1300 = c^2$	Add.
$\sqrt{1300} = c$	Take the positive square root of each side.
$36.1 \approx c$	Use a calculator.

Exercises

Find x.

1. **$\sqrt{18}$ or $3\sqrt{2} \approx 4.2$**
2. **12**
3. **60**
4. **$\frac{1}{3}$**
5. **$\sqrt{1345} \approx 36.7$**
6. **$\sqrt{663} \approx 25.7$**

Use a Pythagorean Triple to find x.

7. **15**
8. **51**
9. **100**

NAME ______________ DATE ________ PERIOD ________

8-2 Study Guide and Intervention *(continued)*

The Pythagorean Theorem and Its Converse

Converse of the Pythagorean Theorem If the sum of the squares of the lengths of the two shorter sides of a triangle equals the square of the lengths of the longest side, then the triangle is a right triangle.

If $a^2 + b^2 = c^2$, then $\triangle ABC$ is a right triangle.

You can also use the lengths of sides to classify a triangle.

if $a^2 + b^2 = c^2$ then $\triangle ABC$ is a right triangle.
if $a^2 + b^2 > c^2$ then $\triangle ABC$ is acute.
if $a^2 + b^2 < c^2$ then $\triangle ABC$ is obtuse.

Example **Determine whether $\triangle PQR$ is a right triangle.**

$a^2 + b^2 \stackrel{?}{=} c^2$	Compare c^2 and $a^2 + b^2$
$10^2 + (10\sqrt{3})^2 \stackrel{?}{=} 20^2$	$a = 10$, $b = 10\sqrt{3}$, $c = 20$
$100 + 300 \stackrel{?}{=} 400$	Simplify.
$400 = 400$ ✓	Add.

Since $c^2 =$ and $a^2 + b^2$, the triangle is a right triangle.

Exercises

Determine whether each set of measures can be the measures of the sides of a triangle. If so, classify the triangle as *acute, obtuse,* or *right*. Justify your answer.

1. 30, 40, 50
yes, right; $50^2 = 30^2 + 40^2$

2. 20, 30, 40
yes, obtuse; $40^2 > 20^2 + 30^2$

3. 18, 24, 30
yes, right; $30^2 = 24^2 + 18^2$

4. 6, 8, 9
yes, acute; $9^2 < 6^2 + 8^2$

5. 6, 12, 18
no; $6 + 12 = 18$

6. 10, 15, 20
yes, obtuse; $20^2 > 10^2 + 15^2$

7. $\sqrt{5}, \sqrt{12}, \sqrt{13}$
yes, acute; $(\sqrt{13})^2 < (\sqrt{5})^2 + (\sqrt{12})^2$

8. $2, \sqrt{8}, \sqrt{12}$
yes, right; $(\sqrt{12})^2 = (\sqrt{8})^2 + 2^2$

9. 9, 40, 41
yes, right; $41^2 = 40^2 + 9^2$

NAME ______________ DATE ________ PERIOD ________

8-2 Skills Practice

The Pythagorean Theorem and Its Converse

Find x.

1. **15**

2.  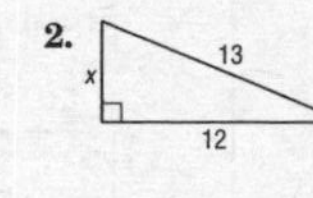
5

3. **$\sqrt{1168} \approx 34.2$**

4. **$\sqrt{468.75} \approx 21.7$**

5. 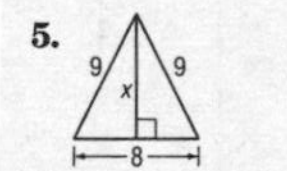 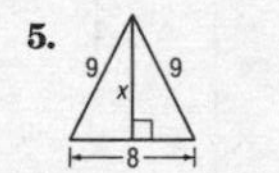 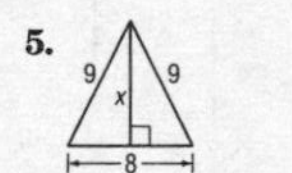 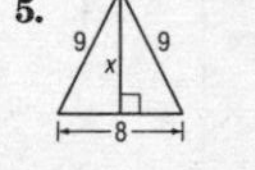 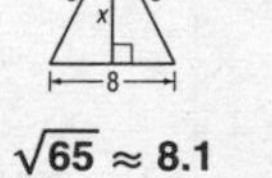 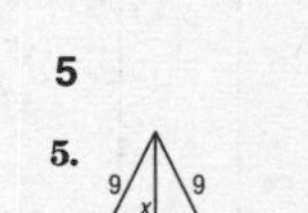
$\sqrt{65} \approx 8.1$

6. **$\sqrt{1157} \approx 34.0$**

Use a Pythagorean Triple to find x.

7. **13**

8. 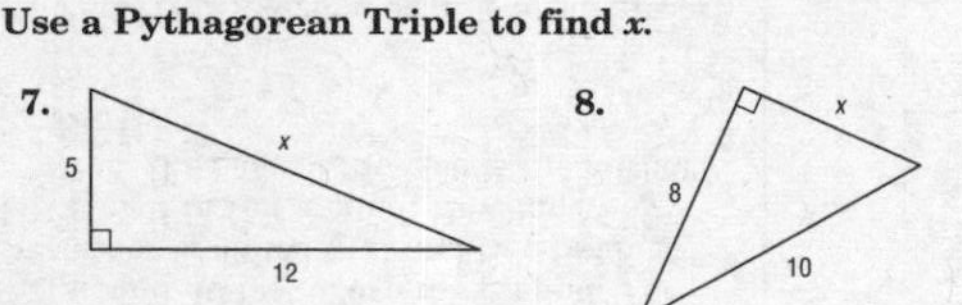 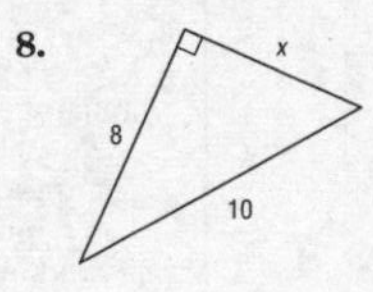
6

9. **16**

10. 
60

11. 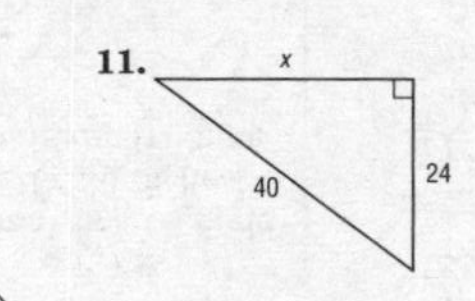
32

12. 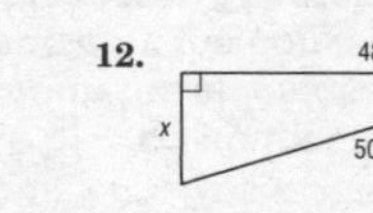  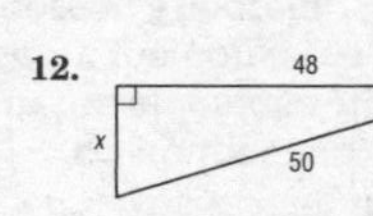
14

Determine whether each set of numbers can be measure of the sides of a triangle. If so, classify the triangle as *acute, obtuse, or right*. Justify your answer.

13. 7, 24, 25
Yes, right triangle $7^2 + 24^2 = 25^2$

14. 8, 14, 20
Yes, obtuse triangle $8^2 + 14^2 < 20^2$

15. 12.5, 13, 26
No, $12.5 + 13 < 26$

16. $3\sqrt{2}, \sqrt{7}, 4$
Yes, acute triangle $(3\sqrt{2})^2 + \sqrt{7}^2 > 4^2$

17. 20, 21, 29
Yes, right triangle $20^2 + 21^2 = 29^2$

18. 32, 35, 70
No, $32 + 35 < 70$

NAME ______________ DATE ________ PERIOD ________

8-2 Practice

The Pythagorean Theorem and Its Converse

Find x.

1. $\sqrt{698} \approx 26.4$
2. $\sqrt{715} \approx 26.7$
3. $\sqrt{595} \approx 24.4$
4. 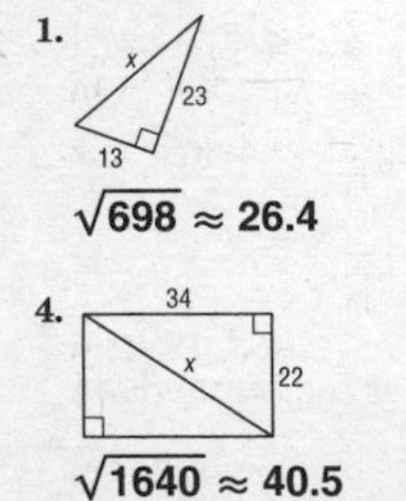

$\sqrt{1640} \approx 40.5$
5. $\sqrt{60} \approx 7.7$
6. $\sqrt{135} \approx 11.6$

Use a Pythagorean Triple to find x.

7. **45**
8. **64**
9. **52**
10. **144**

Determine whether each set of numbers can be measure of the sides of a triangle. If so, classify the triangle as *acute, obtuse, or right*. Justify your answer.

11. 10, 11, 20 **yes, obtuse triangle; $10^2 + 11^2 < 20^2$**
12. 12, 14, 49 **no, $12 + 14 < 49$;**
13. $5\sqrt{2}$, 10, 11 **yes, acute triangle; $(5\sqrt{2})^2 + 10^2 > 11^2$**
14. 21.5, 24, 55.5 **no, $21.5 + 24 < 55.5$**
15. 30, 40, 50 **yes, right triangle; $30^2 + 40^2 = 50^2$**
16. 65, 72, 97 **yes, right triangle; $65^2 + 72^2 = 97^2$**

17. **CONSTRUCTION** The bottom end of a ramp at a warehouse is 10 feet from the base of the main dock and is 11 feet long. How high is the dock? **about 4.6 ft high**

NAME ______________ DATE ________ PERIOD ________

8-2 Word Problem Practice

The Pythagorean Theorem and Its Converse

1. **SIDEWALKS** Construction workers are building a marble sidewalk around a park that is shaped like a right triangle. Each marble slab adds 2 feet to the length of the sidewalk. The workers find that exactly 1071 and 1840 slabs are required to make the sidewalks along the short sides of the park. How many slabs are required to make the sidewalk that runs along the long side of the park?
2129

2. **RIGHT ANGLES** Clyde makes a triangle using three sticks of lengths 20 inches, 21 inches, and 28 inches. Is the triangle a right triangle? Explain.
no; $20^2 + 21^2 \neq 28^2$

3. **TETHERS** To help support a flag pole, a 50-foot-long tether is tied to the pole at a point 40 feet above the ground. The tether is pulled taut and tied to an anchor in the ground. How far away from the base of the pole is the anchor?
30 ft

4. **FLIGHT** An airplane lands at an airport 60 miles east and 25 miles north of where it took off.

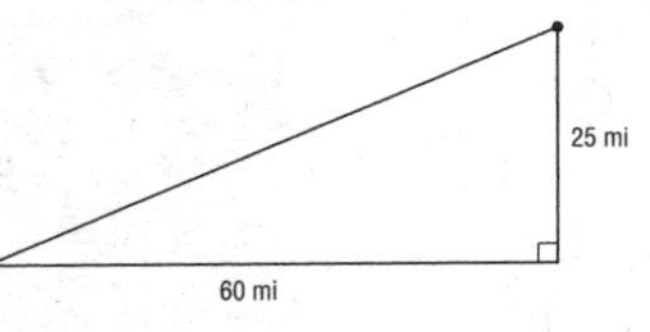

How far apart are the two airports?
65 mi

5. **PYTHAGOREAN TRIPLES** Ms. Jones assigned her fifth-period geometry class the following problem.
Let m and n be two positive integers with $m > n$. Let $a = m^2 - n^2$, $b = 2mn$, and $c = m^2 + n^2$.

a. Show that there is a right triangle with side lengths a, b, and c.
Sample answer: $a^2 + b^2 = (m^2 - n^2)^2 + (2mn)^2 = m^4 - 2m^2n^2 + n^4 + 4m^2n^2 = m^4 + 2m^2n^2 + n^4$ and $c^2 = (m^2 + n^2)^2 = m^4 + 2m^2n^2 + n^4$. This means that $a^2 + b^2 = c^2$, so that a, b, and c do form the sides of a right triangle by the converse of the Pythagorean Theorem.

b. Complete the following table.

m	n	a	b	c
2	1	3	4	5
3	1	**8**	**6**	**10**
3	2	**5**	**12**	**13**
4	1	**15**	**8**	**17**
4	2	**12**	**16**	**20**
4	3	**7**	**24**	**25**
5	1	**24**	**10**	**26**

c. Find a Pythagorean triple that corresponds to a right triangle with a hypotenuse $25^2 = 625$ units long. (*Hint:* Use the table you completed for Exercise b to find two positive integers m and n with $m > n$ and $m^2 + n^2 = 625$.)
Sample answer: Take $m = 24$ and $n = 7$ to get $a = 527$, $b = 336$, and $c = 625$.

NAME ______________________ DATE __________ PERIOD __________

8-2 Enrichment

Converse of a Right Triangle Theorem

You have learned that the measure of the altitude from the vertex of the right angle of a right triangle to its hypotenuse is the geometric mean between the measures of the two segments of the hypotenuse. Is the converse of this theorem true? In order to find out, it will help to rewrite the original theorem in if-then form as follows.

If $\triangle ABQ$ is a right triangle with right angle at Q, then QP is the geometric mean between AP and PB, where P is between A and B and $\overline{QP}$ is perpendicular to $\overline{AB}$.

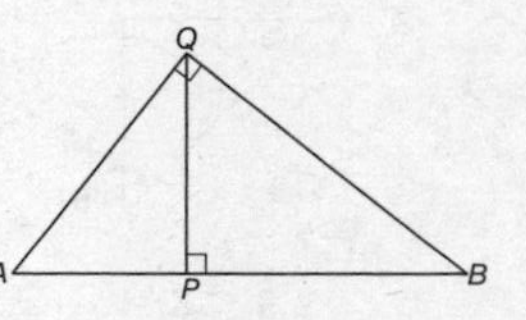

1. Write the converse of the if-then form of the theorem.

   If QP is the geometric mean between AP and PB, where P is between A and B and $\overline{QP} \perp \overline{AB}$, then $\triangle ABQ$ is a right triangle with right angle at Q.

2. Is the converse of the original theorem true? Refer to the figure at the right to explain your answer.

   Yes; $(PQ)^2 = (AP)(PB)$ implies that $\frac{PQ}{AP} = \frac{PB}{PQ}$. Since both $\angle APQ$ and $\angle QPB$ are right angles, they are congruent. Therefore $\triangle APQ \sim \triangle QPB$ by SAS similarity. So $\angle A \cong \angle PQB$ and $\angle AQP \cong \angle B$. But the acute angles of $\triangle AQP$ are complementary and $m\angle AQB = m\angle AQP + m\angle PQB$. Hence $m\angle AQB = 90$ and $\triangle AQB$ is a right triangle with right angle at Q.

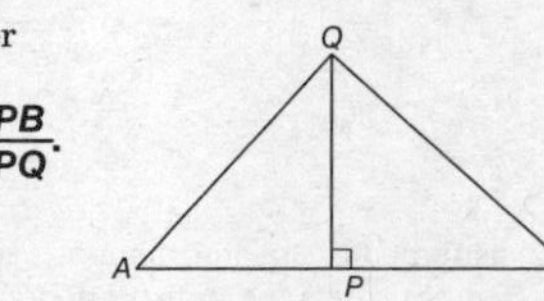

You may find it interesting to examine the other theorems in Chapter 8 to see whether their converses are true or false. You will need to restate the theorems carefully in order to write their converses.

NAME ______________________ DATE __________ PERIOD __________

8-2 Spreadsheet Activity

Pythagorean Triples

You can use a spreadsheet to determine whether three whole numbers form a Pythagorean triple.

Example 1 **Use a spreadsheet to determine whether the numbers 12, 16, and 20 form a Pythagorean triple.**

Step 1 In cell A1, enter 12. In cell B1, enter 16 and in cell C1, enter 20. *The longest side should be entered in column C.*

Step 2 In cell D1, enter an equals sign followed by IF(A1^2+B1^2=C1^2,“YES”,“NO”). This will return “YES” if the set of numbers is a Pythagorean triple and will return “NO” if it is not.

Triples.xls

◇	A	B	C	D
1	12	16	20	YES
2	3	6	12	NO

Sheet 1 / Sheet 2 / Sheet 3

The numbers 12, 16, and 20 form a Pythagorean triple.

Example 2 **Use a spreadsheet to determine whether the numbers 3, 6, and 12 form a Pythagorean triple.**

Step 1 In cell A2, enter 3, in cell B2, enter 6, and in cell C2, enter 12.

Step 2 Click on the bottom right corner of cell D1 and drag it to D2. This will determine whether or not the set of numbers is a Pythagorean triple.

The numbers 3, 6, and 12 do not form a Pythagorean triple.

Exercises

Use a spreadsheet to determine whether each set of numbers forms a Pythagorean triple.

1. 14, 48, 50 **yes**
2. 16, 30, 34 **yes**
3. 5, 5, 9 **no**
4. 4, 5, 7 **no**
5. 18, 24, 30 **yes**
6. 10, 24, 26 **yes**
7. 25, 60, 65 **yes**
8. 2, 4, 5 **no**
9. 19, 21, 22 **no**
10. 18, 80, 82 **yes**
11. 5, 12, 13 **yes**
12. 20, 48, 52 **yes**

Lesson 8-2

Answers

NAME ________________ DATE ________ PERIOD ________

8-3 Study Guide and Intervention

Special Right Triangles

Properties of 45°-45°-90° Triangles The sides of a 45°-45°-90° right triangle have a special relationship.

Example 1 **If the leg of a 45°-45°-90° right triangle is x units, show that the hypotenuse is $x\sqrt{2}$ units.**

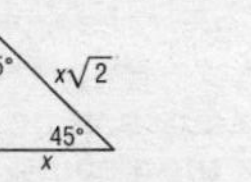

Using the Pythagorean Theorem with $a = b = x$, then

$c^2 = a^2 + b^2$
$c^2 = x^2 + x^2$
$c^2 = 2x^2$
$c = \sqrt{2x^2}$
$c = x\sqrt{2}$

Example 2 **In a 45°-45°-90° right triangle the hypotenuse is $\sqrt{2}$ times the leg. If the hypotenuse is 6 units, find the length of each leg.**

The hypotenuse is $\sqrt{2}$ times the leg, so divide the length of the hypotenuse by $\sqrt{2}$.

$a = \frac{6}{\sqrt{2}}$
$= \frac{6}{\sqrt{2}} \cdot \frac{\sqrt{2}}{\sqrt{2}}$
$= \frac{6\sqrt{2}}{2}$
$= 3\sqrt{2}$ units

Exercises

Find x.

1. **$8\sqrt{2} \approx 11.3$**
2. **3**
3. **$4\sqrt{2} \approx 5.7$**
4. **$9\sqrt{2} \approx 12.7$**
5. **$8\sqrt{2} \approx 11.3$**
6. **24**

7. If a 45°-45°-90° triangle has a hypotenuse length of 12, find the leg length. **$6\sqrt{2} \approx 8.5$**

8. Determine the length of the leg of 45°-45°-90° triangle with a hypotenuse length of 25 inches. **$\frac{25\sqrt{2}}{2}$ in. ≈ 17.7 in.**

9. Find the length of the hypotenuse of a 45°-45°-90° triangle with a leg length of 14 centimeters. **$14\sqrt{2}$ cm ≈ 19.8 cm**

NAME ________________ DATE ________ PERIOD ________

8-3 Study Guide and Intervention *(continued)*

Special Right Triangles

Properties of 30°-60°-90° Triangles The sides of a 30°-60°-90° right triangle also have a special relationship.

Example 1 **In a 30°-60°-90° right triangle the hypotenuse is twice the shorter leg. Show that the longer leg is $\sqrt{3}$ times the shorter leg.**

$\triangle MNQ$ is a 30°-60°-90° right triangle, and the length of the hypotenuse $\overline{MN}$ is two times the length of the shorter side $\overline{NQ}$. Use the Pythagorean Theorem.

$a^2 = (2x)^2 - x^2$	$a^2 = c^2 - b^2$
$a^2 = 4x^2 - x^2$	Multiply.
$a^2 = 3x^2$	Subtract.
$a = \sqrt{3x^2}$	Take the positive square root of each side.
$a = x\sqrt{3}$	Simplify.

Example 2 **In a 30°-60°-90° right triangle, the hypotenuse is 5 centimeters. Find the lengths of the other two sides of the triangle.**

If the hypotenuse of a 30°-60°-90° right triangle is 5 centimeters, then the length of the shorter leg is one-half of 5, or 2.5 centimeters. The length of the longer leg is $\sqrt{3}$ times the length of the shorter leg, or $(2.5)(\sqrt{3})$ centimeters.

Exercises

Find x and y.

1. 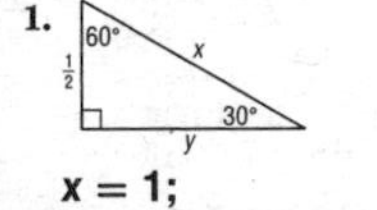
$x = 1$; $y = 0.5\sqrt{3} \approx 0.9$

2. **$x = 8\sqrt{3} \approx 13.9$; $y = 16$**

3. **$x = 5.5$; $y = 5.5\sqrt{3} \approx 9.5$**

4. 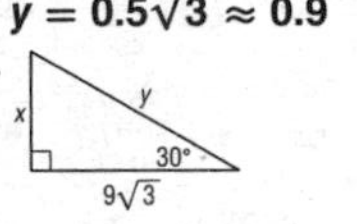
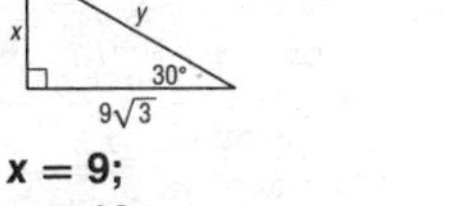
$x = 9$; $y = 18$

5. **$x = 4\sqrt{3} \approx 6.9$; $y = 8\sqrt{3} \approx 13.9$**

6. **$x = 10\sqrt{3} \approx 17.3$; $y = 10$**

7. An equilateral triangle has an altitude length of 36 feet. Determine the length of a side of the triangle. **$24\sqrt{3}$ feet ≈ 41.6 ft**

8. Find the length of the side of an equilateral triangle that has an altitude length of 45 centimeters. **$30\sqrt{3}$ cm ≈ 52 cm**

NAME ______________ DATE ________ PERIOD ________

8-3 Skills Practice

Special Right Triangles

Find x.

1. 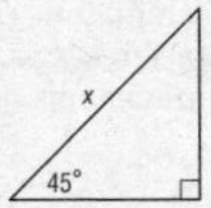 $25\sqrt{2}$
2. 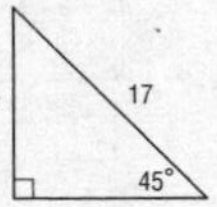 $8.5\sqrt{2}$ or $\frac{17\sqrt{2}}{2}$
3. 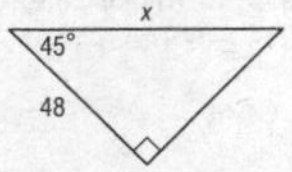 $48\sqrt{2}$
4. 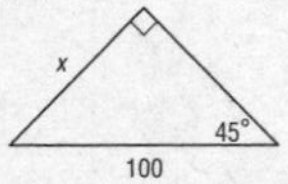 $50\sqrt{2}$
5. 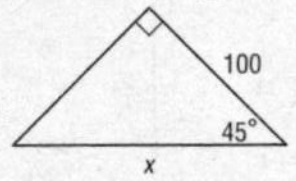 $100\sqrt{2}$
6. 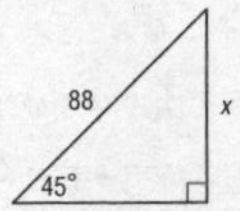 $44\sqrt{2}$

7. Determine the length of the leg of 45°-45°-90° triangle with a hypotenuse length of 26. $13\sqrt{2}$

8. Find the length of the hypotenuse of a 45°-45°-90° triangle with a leg length of 50 centimeters.
$50\sqrt{2}$ cm

Find x and y.

9. 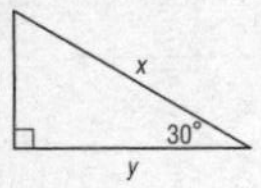 $22; 11\sqrt{3}$
10. 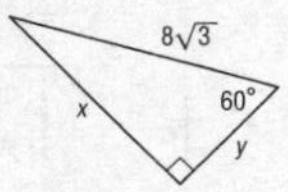 $12; 4\sqrt{3}$
11. 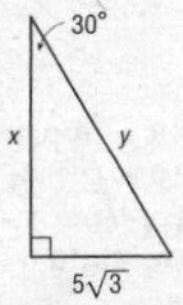 $15; 10\sqrt{3}$
12. 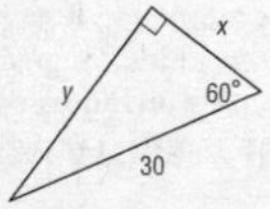 $15; 15\sqrt{3}$
13. 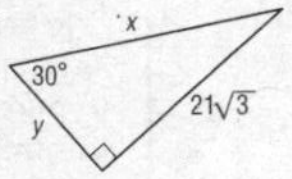 $42; 21$
14. 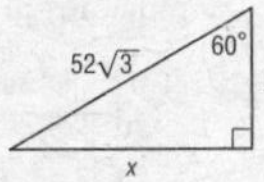 $78; 26\sqrt{3}$

$42\sqrt{3}$, 63

15. An equilateral triangle has an altitude length of 27 feet. Determine the length of a side of the triangle.
$18\sqrt{3}$

16. Find the length of the side of an equilateral triangle that has an altitude length of $11\sqrt{3}$ feet.
22

NAME ______________ DATE ________ PERIOD ________

8-3 Practice

Special Right Triangles

Find x.

1. 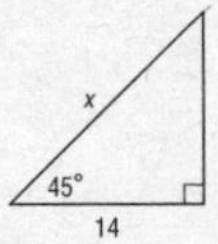 $14\sqrt{2}$
2. 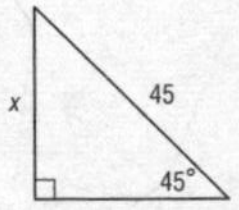 $22.5\sqrt{2}$ or $\frac{45\sqrt{2}}{2}$
3. 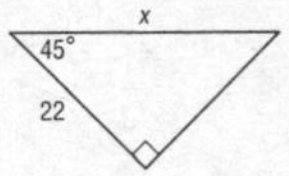 $22\sqrt{2}$
4. 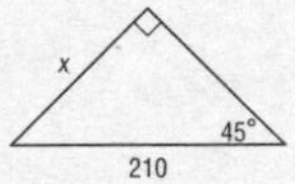 $105\sqrt{2}$
5. 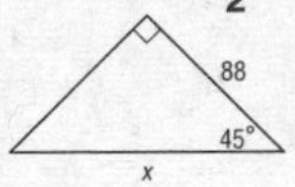 $88\sqrt{2}$
6. 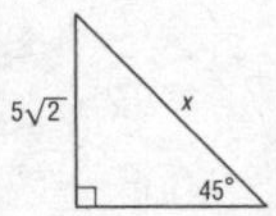 10

Find x and y.

7. 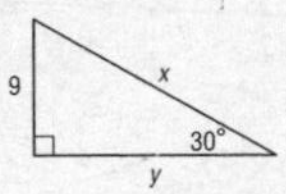 $x = 18$; $y = 9\sqrt{3}$
8. 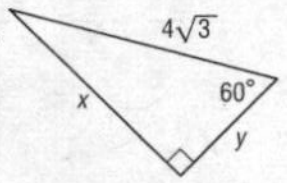 $x = 6$; $y = 2\sqrt{3}$
9. 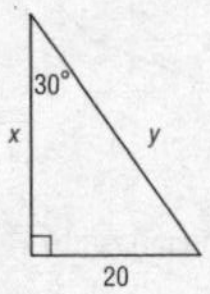 $x = 20\sqrt{3}$; $y = 40$
10. 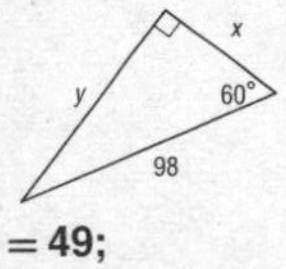 $x = 49$; $y = 49\sqrt{3}$

11. Determine the length of the leg of 45°-45°-90° triangle with a hypotenuse length of 38.
$19\sqrt{2}$

12. Find the length of the hypotenuse of a 45°-45°-90° triangle with a leg length of 77 centimeters. $77\sqrt{2}$ cm

13. An equilateral triangle has an altitude length of 33 feet. Determine the length of a side of the triangle. $22\sqrt{3}$ ft

14. **BOTANICAL GARDENS** One of the displays at a botanical garden is an herb garden planted in the shape of a square. The square measures 6 yards on each side. Visitors can view the herbs from a diagonal pathway through the garden. How long is the pathway?
$6\sqrt{2}$ yd or about 8.49 yd

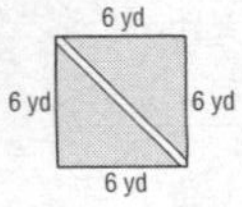

Lesson 8-3

Answers

NAME ______________________ DATE __________ PERIOD __________

8-3 Word Problem Practice

Special Right Triangles

1. ORIGAMI A square piece of paper 150 millimeters on a side is folded in half along a diagonal. The result is a 45°-45°-90° triangle. What is the length of the hypotenuse of this triangle?

$150\sqrt{2}$ mm

2. ESCALATORS A 40-foot-long escalator rises from the first floor to the second floor of a shopping mall. The escalator makes a 30° angle with the horizontal.

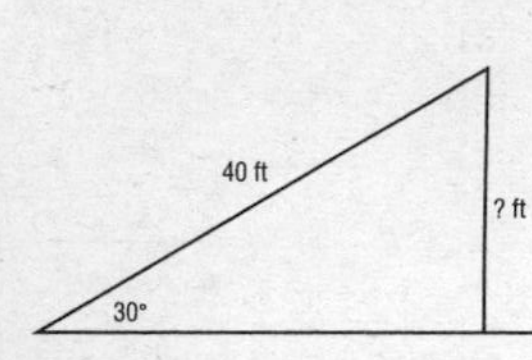

How high above the first floor is the second floor?

20ft

3. HEXAGONS A box of chocolates shaped like a regular hexagon is placed snugly inside of a rectangular box as shown in the figure.

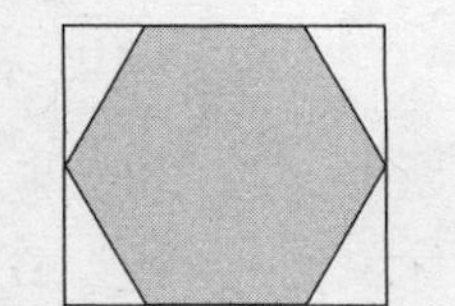

If the side length of the hexagon is 3 inches, what are the dimensions of the rectangular box?

6 in. by $3\sqrt{3}$ in.

4. WINDOWS A large stained glass window is constructed from six 30°-60°-90° triangles as shown in the figure.

3 m

What is the height of the window?

$\frac{4\sqrt{3}}{3}$ m ≈ 2.31 m

5. MOVIES Kim and Yolanda are watching a movie in a movie theater. Yolanda is sitting x feet from the screen and Kim is 15 feet behind Yolanda.

30° 45°
15 ft x ft

The angle that Kim's line of sight to the top of the screen makes with the horizontal is 30°. The angle that Yolanda's line of sight to the top of the screen makes with the horizontal is 45°.

a. How high is the top of the screen in terms of x?

x ft

b. What is $\frac{x + 15}{x}$?

$\sqrt{3}$ ft

altitude $x\sqrt{3}$
short side x

c. How far is Yolanda from the screen? Round your answer to the nearest tenth.

20.5 ft

15+x

NAME ______________________ DATE __________ PERIOD __________

8-3 Enrichment

Constructing Values of Square Roots

The diagram at the right shows a right isosceles triangle with two legs of length 1 inch. By the Pythagorean Theorem, the length of the hypotenuse is $\sqrt{2}$ inches. By constructing an adjacent right triangle with legs of $\sqrt{2}$ inches and 1 inch, you can create a segment of length $\sqrt{3}$.

By continuing this process as shown below, you can construct a "wheel" of square roots. This wheel is called the "Wheel of Theodorus" after a Greek philosopher who lived about 400 B.C.

Continue constructing the wheel until you make a segment of length $\sqrt{18}$.

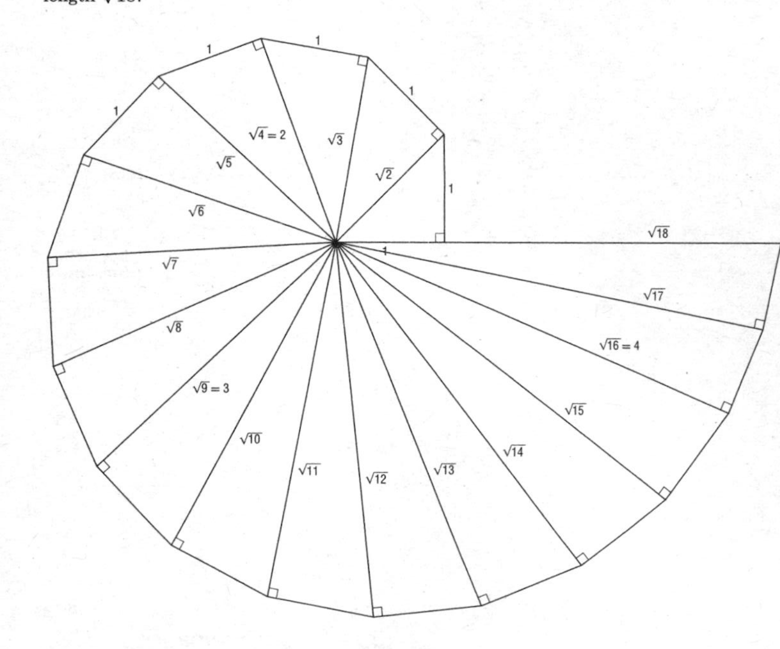

NAME ______________________ DATE ____________ PERIOD ________

8-4 Study Guide and Intervention

Trigonometry

Trigonometric Ratios The ratio of the lengths of two sides of a right triangle is called a **trigonometric ratio.** The three most common ratios are **sine, cosine,** and **tangent,** which are abbreviated *sin, cos,* and *tan,* respectively.

$\sin R = \dfrac{\text{leg opposite } \angle R}{\text{hypotenuse}} = \dfrac{r}{t}$ $\quad\cos R = \dfrac{\text{leg adjacent to } \angle R}{\text{hypotenuse}} = \dfrac{s}{t}$ $\quad\tan R = \dfrac{\text{leg opposite } \angle R}{\text{leg adjacent to } \angle R} = \dfrac{r}{s}$

Example Find sin *A*, cos *A*, and tan *A*. Express each ratio as a fraction and a decimal to the nearest hundredth.

$\sin A = \dfrac{\text{opposite leg}}{\text{hypotenuse}} = \dfrac{BC}{BA} = \dfrac{5}{13} \approx 0.38$

$\cos A = \dfrac{\text{adjacent leg}}{\text{hypotenuse}} = \dfrac{AC}{AB} = \dfrac{12}{13} \approx 0.92$

$\tan A = \dfrac{\text{opposite leg}}{\text{adjacent leg}} = \dfrac{BC}{AC} = \dfrac{5}{12} \approx 0.42$

Exercises

Find sin *J*, cos *J*, tan *J*, sin *L*, cos *L*, and tan *L*. Express each ratio as a fraction and as a decimal to the nearest hundredth if necessary.

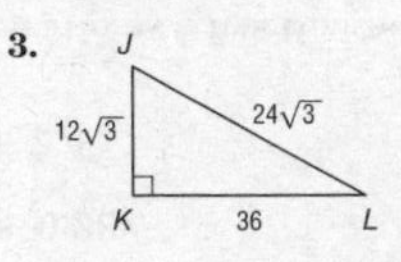
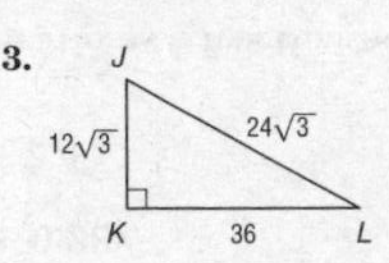
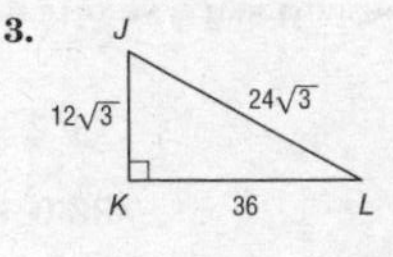

1. (JK = 16, KL = 12, JL = 20)

sin $J = \frac{12}{20} = 0.6$; cos $J = \frac{16}{20} = 0.8$; tan $J = \frac{12}{16} = 0.75$; sin $L = \frac{16}{20} = 0.8$; cos $L = \frac{12}{20} = 0.6$; tan $L = \frac{16}{12} \approx 1.33$

2. (JK = 32, KL = 24, JL = 40)

sin $J = \frac{24}{40} = 0.6$; cos $J = \frac{32}{40} = 0.8$; tan $J = \frac{24}{32} = 0.75$; sin $L = \frac{32}{40} = 0.8$; cos $L = \frac{24}{32} = 0.6$; tan $L = \frac{32}{24} \approx 1.33$

3. (JK = $12\sqrt{3}$, KL = 36, JL = $24\sqrt{3}$)

sin $J = \frac{36}{24\sqrt{3}} \approx 0.87$; cos $J = \frac{12\sqrt{3}}{24\sqrt{3}} = 0.5$; tan $J = \frac{36}{12\sqrt{3}} \approx 1.73$; sin $L = \frac{12\sqrt{3}}{24\sqrt{3}} = 0.5$; cos $L = \frac{36}{24\sqrt{3}} \approx 0.87$; tan $L = \frac{12\sqrt{3}}{36} \approx 0.58$

NAME ______________________ DATE ____________ PERIOD ________

8-4 Study Guide and Intervention *(continued)*

Trigonometry

Use Inverse Trigonometric Ratios You can use a calculator and the sine, cosine, or tangent to find the measure of the angle, called the **inverse** of the trigonometric ratio.

Example Use a calculator to find the measure of $\angle T$ to the nearest tenth.

The measures given are those of the leg opposite $\angle T$ and the hypotenuse, so write an equation using the sine ratio.

$\sin T = \dfrac{opp}{hyp}$ $\quad \sin T = \dfrac{29}{34}$

If $\sin T = \dfrac{29}{34}$, then $\sin^{-1} \dfrac{29}{34} = m\angle T$.

Use a calculator. So, $m\angle T \approx 58.5$.

Exercises

Use a calculator to find the measure of $\angle T$ to the nearest tenth.

1. **35.5°**
2. **22.9°**
3. **67°**
4. **71.5°**
5. **75°**
6. **30.5°**

NAME ______________________ DATE __________ PERIOD __________

8-4 Skills Practice

Trigonometry

Find sin R, cos R, tan R, sin S, cos S, and tan S. Express each ratio as a fraction and as a decimal to the nearest hundredth.

1. $r = 16, s = 30, t = 34$

$\sin R = \frac{8}{17} \approx 0.47$; $\cos R = \frac{15}{17} \approx 0.88$; $\tan R = \frac{8}{15} \approx 0.53$; $\sin S = \frac{15}{17} \approx 0.88$; $\cos S = \frac{8}{17} \approx 0.47$; $\tan S = \frac{15}{8} \approx 1.88$

2. $r = 10, s = 24, t = 26$

$\sin R = \frac{5}{13} \approx 0.38$; $\cos R = \frac{12}{13} \approx 0.92$; $\tan R = \frac{5}{12} \approx 0.42$; $\sin S = \frac{12}{13} \approx 0.92$; $\cos S = \frac{5}{13} \approx 0.38$; $\tan S = \frac{12}{5} \approx 2.4$

Use a special right triangle to express each trigonometric ratio as a fraction and as a decimal to the nearest hundredth if necessary.

3. sin 30° $\frac{1}{2}$; 0.5
4. tan 45° 1
5. cos 60° $\frac{1}{2}$; 0.5
6. sin 60° $\frac{\sqrt{3}}{2}$; 0.87
7. tan 30° $\frac{\sqrt{3}}{3}$; 0.58
8. cos 45° $\frac{\sqrt{2}}{2}$; 0.71

Find x. Round to the nearest hundredth if necessary.

9. $x = 5.09$

10. 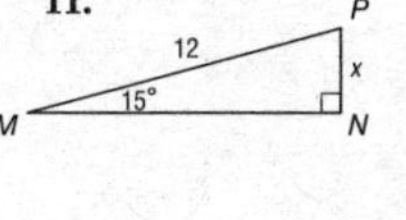

$x = 13.47$

11. 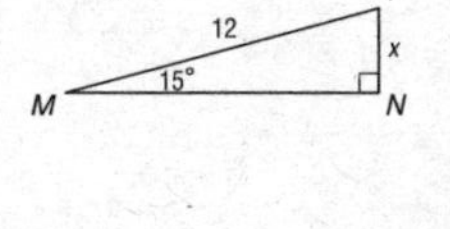

$x = 3.11$

Use a calculator to find the measure of $\angle B$ to the nearest tenth.

12. 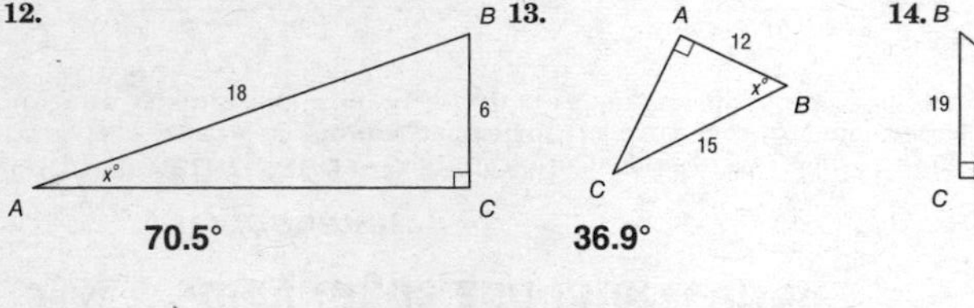

70.5°

13. 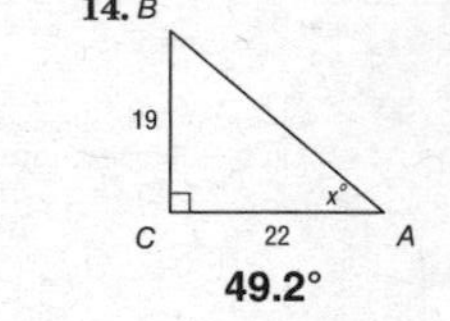

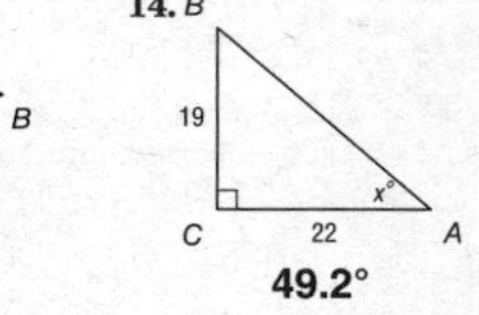

36.9°

14. 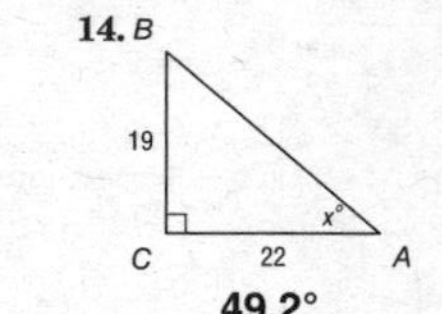

49.2°

NAME ______________________ DATE __________ PERIOD __________

8-4 Practice

Trigonometry

Find sin L, cos L, tan L, sin M, cos M, and tan M. Express each ratio as a fraction and as a decimal to the nearest hundredth.

1. $\ell = 15, m = 36, n = 39$

$\sin L = \frac{5}{13} \approx 0.38$; $\cos L = \frac{12}{13} \approx 0.92$; $\tan L = \frac{5}{12} \approx 0.42$; $\sin M = \frac{12}{13} \approx 0.92$; $\cos M = \frac{5}{13} \approx 0.38$; $\tan M = \frac{12}{5} \approx 2.4$

2. $\ell = 12, m = 12\sqrt{3}, n = 24$

$\sin L = \frac{1}{2} = 0.50$; $\cos L = \frac{\sqrt{3}}{2} \approx 0.87$; $\tan L = \frac{1}{\sqrt{3}}$ or $\frac{\sqrt{3}}{3} \approx 0.58$; $\sin M = \frac{\sqrt{3}}{2} \approx 0.87$; $\cos M = \frac{1}{2} = 0.50$; $\tan M = \sqrt{3} \approx 1.73$

Find x. Round to the nearest hundredth.

3. 22.55
4. 25.36
5. 24.15

Use a calculator to find the measure of $\angle B$ to the nearest tenth.

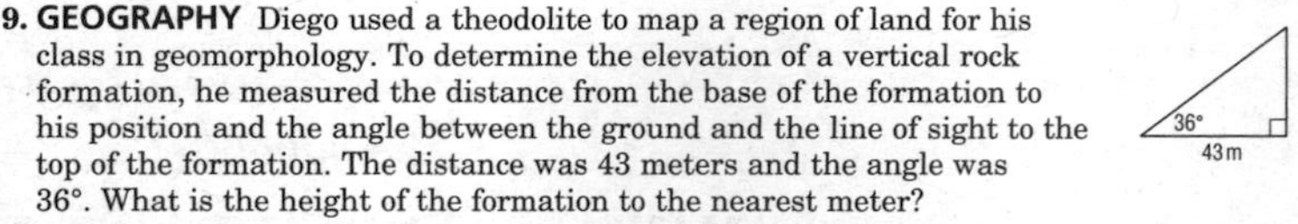

6. 60.3°
7. 33.6°
8. 79.7°

9. **GEOGRAPHY** Diego used a theodolite to map a region of land for his class in geomorphology. To determine the elevation of a vertical rock formation, he measured the distance from the base of the formation to his position and the angle between the ground and the line of sight to the top of the formation. The distance was 43 meters and the angle was 36°. What is the height of the formation to the nearest meter? **31 m**

NAME ______________________ DATE ____________ PERIOD ____________

8-4 Word Problem Practice

Trigonometry

1. RADIO TOWERS Kay is standing near a 200-foot-high radio tower.

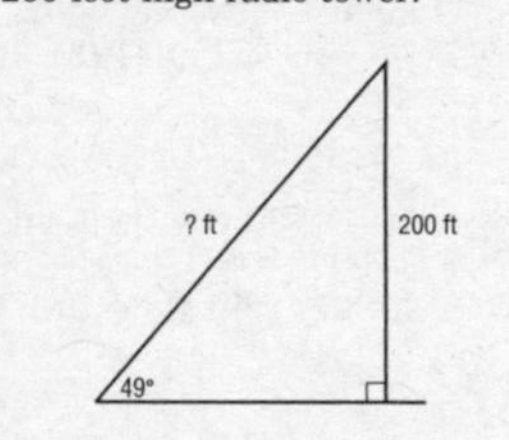

Use the information in the figure to determine how far Kay is from the top of the tower. Express your answer as a trigonometric function.

$$\frac{\mathbf{200}}{\mathbf{\sin 49°}}$$

2. RAMPS A 60-foot ramp rises from the first floor to the second floor of a parking garage. The ramp makes a 15° angle with the ground.

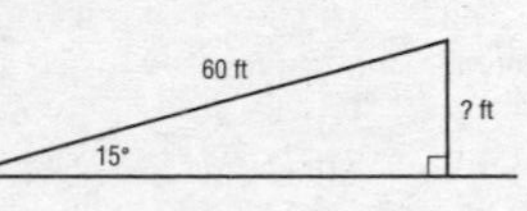

How high above the first floor is the second floor? Express your answer as a trigonometric function.

60 sin 15°

3. TRIGONOMETRY Melinda and Walter were both solving the same trigonometry problem. However, after they finished their computations, Melinda said the answer was 52 sin 27° and Walter said the answer was 52 cos 63°. Could they both be correct? Explain.

Yes, they are both correct. Because 27 + 63 = 90, the sine of 27° is the same ratio as the cosine of 63°.

4. LINES Jasmine draws line m on a coordinate plane.

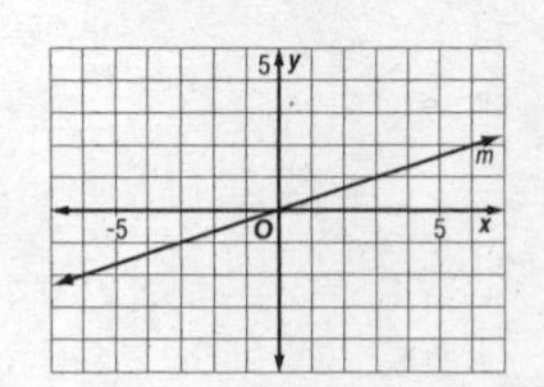

What angle does m make with the x-axis? Round your answer to the nearest degree.

18°

5. NEIGHBORS Amy, Barry, and Chris live on the same block. Chris lives up the street and around the corner from Amy, and Barry lives at the corner between Amy and Chris. The three homes are the vertices of a right triangle.

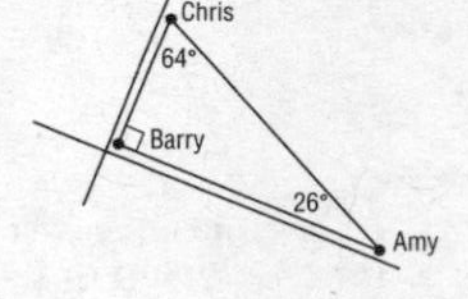

a. Give two trigonometric expressions for the ratio of Barry's distance from Amy to Chris' distance from Amy.

cos 26° or sin 64°

b. Give two trigonometric expressions for the ratio of Barry's distance from Chris to Amy's distance from Chris.

cos 64° or sin 26°

c. Give a trigonometric expression for the ratio of Amy's distance from Barry to Chris' distance from Barry.

tan 64°

NAME ______________________ DATE ____________ PERIOD ____________

8-4 Enrichment

Sine and Cosine of Angles

The following diagram can be used to obtain approximate values for the sine and cosine of angles from 0° to 90°. The radius of the circle is 1. So, the sine and cosine values can be read directly from the vertical and horizontal axes.

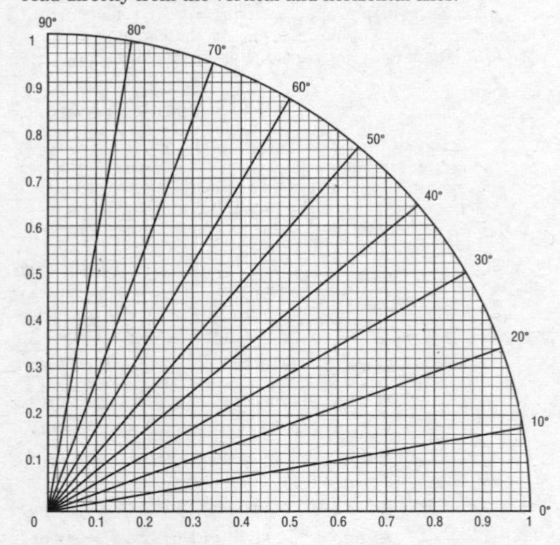

Example **Find approximate values for sin 40° and cos 40°. Consider the triangle formed by the segment marked 40°, as illustrated by the shaded triangle at right.**

$\sin 40° = \frac{a}{c} \approx \frac{0.64}{1}$ or 0.64 $\cos 40° = \frac{b}{c} \approx \frac{0.77}{1}$ or 0.77

1. Use the diagram above to complete the chart of values.

$x°$	0°	10°	20°	30°	40°	50°	60°	70°	80°	90°
sin $x°$	**0**	**0.17**	**0.34**	**0.5**	0.64	**0.77**	**0.87**	**0.94**	**0.98**	**1**
cos $x°$	**1**	**0.98**	**0.94**	**0.87**	0.77	**0.64**	**0.5**	**0.34**	**0.17**	**0**

2. Compare the sine and cosine of two complementary angles (angles with a sum of 90°). What do you notice?

The sine of an angle is equal to the cosine of the complement of the angle.

Lesson 8-4

Answers

NAME ________________ DATE ________ PERIOD ________

8-5 Study Guide and Intervention

Angles of Elevation and Depression

Angles of Elevation and Depression Many real-world problems that involve looking up to an object can be described in terms of an **angle of elevation,** which is the angle between an observer's line of sight and a horizontal line.

When an observer is looking down, the **angle of depression** is the angle between the observer's line of sight and a horizontal line.

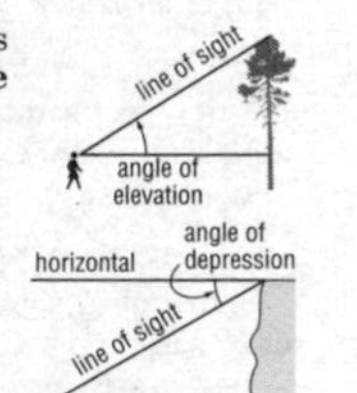

Example **The angle of elevation from point A to the top of a cliff is 34°. If point A is 1000 feet from the base of the cliff, how high is the cliff?**

Let x = the height of the cliff.

$\tan 34° = \frac{x}{1000}$ $\quad \tan = \frac{\text{opposite}}{\text{adjacent}}$

$1000(\tan 34°) = x$ $\quad$ Multiply each side by 1000.

$674.5 \approx x$ $\quad$ Use a calculator.

The height of the cliff is about 674.5 feet.

Exercises

1. **HILL TOP** The angle of elevation from point A to the top of a hill is 49°. If point A is 400 feet from the base of the hill, how high is the hill?
   460 ft

2. **SUN** Find the angle of elevation of the Sun when a 12.5-meter-tall telephone pole casts an 18-meter-long shadow.
   35°

3. **SKIING** A ski run is 1000 yards long with a vertical drop of 208 yards. Find the angle of depression from the top of the ski run to the bottom.
   12°

4. **AIR TRAFFIC** From the top of a 120-foot-high tower, an air traffic controller observes an airplane on the runway at an angle of depression of 19°. How far from the base of the tower is the airplane?
   348.5 ft

NAME ________________ DATE ________ PERIOD ________

8-5 Study Guide and Intervention *(continued)*

Angles of Elevation and Depression

Two Angles of Elevation or Depression Angles of elevation or depression to two different objects can be used to estimate distance between those objects. The angles from two different positions of observation to the same object can be used to estimate the height of the object.

Example **To estimate the height of a garage, Jason sights the top of the garage at a 42° angle of elevation. He then steps back 20 feet and sites the top at a 10° angle. If Jason is 6 feet tall, how tall is the garage to the nearest foot?**

$\triangle ABC$ and $\triangle ABD$ are right triangles. We can determine $AB = x$ and $CB = y$, and $DB = y + 20$.

Use $\triangle ABC$. $\quad$ $\tan 42° = \frac{x}{y}$ or $y \tan 42° = x$

Use $\triangle ABD$. $\quad$ $\tan 10° = \frac{x}{y + 20}$ or $(y + 20) \tan 10° = x$

Substitute the value for x from $\triangle ABD$ in the equation for $\triangle ABC$ and solve for y.

$y \tan 42° = (y + 20) \tan 10°$

$y \tan 42° = y \tan 10° + 20 \tan 10°$

$y \tan 42° - y \tan 10° = 20 \tan 10°$

$y (\tan 42° - \tan 10°) = 20 \tan 10°$

$y = \frac{20 \tan 10°}{\tan 42° - \tan 10°} \approx 4.87$

If $y \approx 4.87$, then $x = 4.87 \tan 42°$ or about 4.4 feet. Add Jason's height, so the garage is about 4.4 + 6 or 10.4 feet tall.

Exercises

1. **CLIFF** Sarah stands on the ground and sights the top of a steep cliff at a 60° angle of elevation. She then steps back 50 meters and sights the top of the steep cliff at a 30° angle. If Sarah is 1.8 meters tall, how tall is the steep cliff to the nearest meter?
   about 45 meters

2. **BALLOON** The angle of depression from a hot air balloon in the air to a person on the ground is 36°. If the person steps back 10 feet, the new angle of depression is 25°. If the person is 6 feet tall, how far off the ground is the hot air balloon?
   about 19 feet

Lesson 8-5

NAME ____________ DATE ________ PERIOD ________

8-5 Skills Practice

Angles of Elevation and Depression

Name the angle of depression or angle of elevation in each figure.

1. 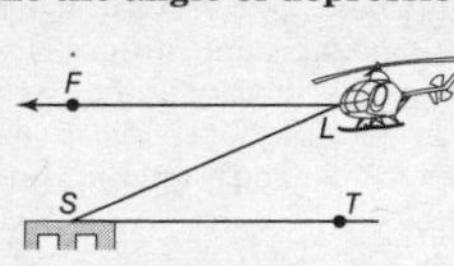

∠FLS; ∠TSL

2. *∠RTW; ∠SWT*

3. 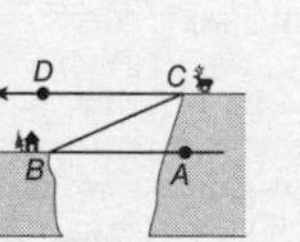

∠DCB; ∠ABC

4. 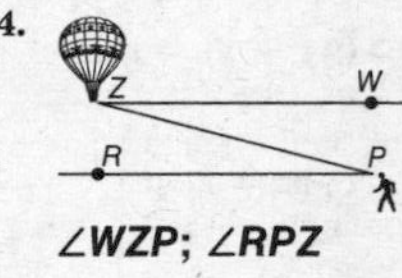

∠WZP; ∠RPZ

5. **MOUNTAIN BIKING** On a mountain bike trip along the Gemini Bridges Trail in Moab, Utah, Nabuko stopped on the canyon floor to get a good view of the twin sandstone bridges. Nabuko is standing about 60 meters from the base of the canyon cliff, and the natural arch bridges are about 100 meters up the canyon wall. If her line of sight is 5 metres above the ground, what is the angle of elevation to the top of the bridges? Round to the nearest tenth degree.
about 57.7°

6. **SHADOWS** Suppose the sun casts a shadow off a 35-foot building. If the angle of elevation to the sun is 60°, how long is the shadow to the nearest tenth of a foot?
about 20.2 ft

7. **BALLOONING** Angie sees a hot air balloon in the sky from her spot on the ground. The angle of elevation from Angie to the balloon is 40°. If she steps back 200 feet, the new angle of elevation is 10°. If Angie is 5.5 feet tall, how far off the ground is the hot air balloon?
about 50.1 ft

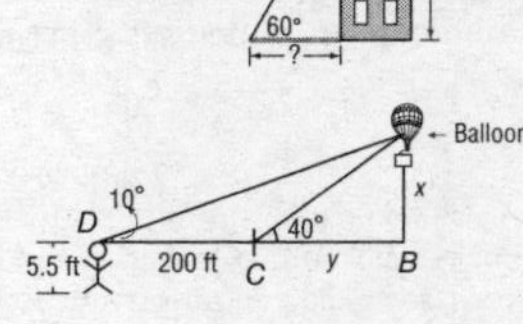

8. **INDIRECT MEASUREMENT** Kyle is at the end of a pier 30 feet above the ocean. His eye level is 3 feet above the pier. He is using binoculars to watch a whale surface. If the angle of depression of the whale is 20°, how far is the whale from Kyle's binoculars? Round to the nearest tenth foot.
about 96.5 ft

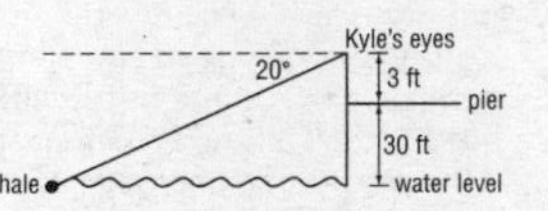

NAME ____________ DATE ________ PERIOD ________

8-5 Practice

Angles of Elevation and Depression

Name the angle of depression or angle of elevation in each figure.

1. *∠TRZ; ∠YZR*

2. 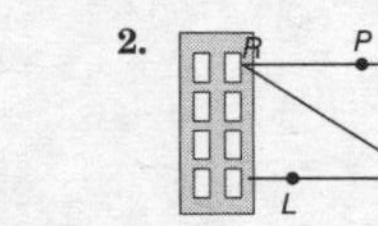

∠PRM; ∠LMR

3. **WATER TOWERS** A student can see a water tower from the closest point of the soccer field at San Lobos High School. The edge of the soccer field is about 110 feet from the water tower and the water tower stands at a height of 32.5 feet. What is the angle of elevation if the eye level of the student viewing the tower from the edge of the soccer field is 6 feet above the ground? Round to the nearest tenth.
about 13.5°

4. **CONSTRUCTION** A roofer props a ladder against a wall so that the top of the ladder reaches a 30-foot roof that needs repair. If the angle of elevation from the bottom of the ladder to the roof is 55°, how far is the ladder from the base of the wall? Round your answer to the nearest foot.
about 21 ft

5. **TOWN ORDINANCES** The town of Belmont restricts the height of flagpoles to 25 feet on any property. Lindsay wants to determine whether her school is in compliance with the regulation. Her eye level is 5.5 feet from the ground and she stands 36 feet from the flagpole. If the angle of elevation is about 25°, what is the height of the flagpole to the nearest tenth?
about 22.3 ft

6. **GEOGRAPHY** Stephan is standing on the ground by a mesa in the Painted Desert. Stephan is 1.8 meters tall and sights the top of the mesa at 29°. Stephan steps back 100 meters and sights the top at 25°. How tall is the mesa?
about 296 m

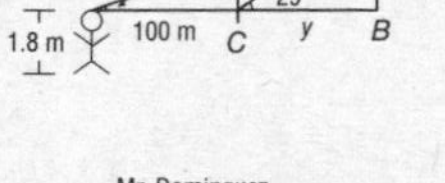

7. **INDIRECT MEASUREMENT** Mr. Dominguez is standing on a 40-foot ocean bluff near his home. He can see his two dogs on the beach below. If his line of sight is 6 feet above the ground and the angles of depression to his dogs are 34° and 48°, how far apart are the dogs to the nearest foot?
about 27 ft

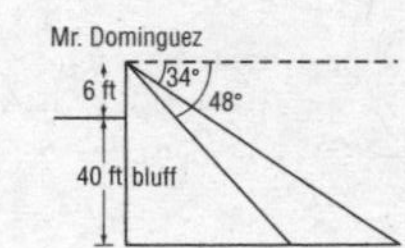

NAME ______________________ DATE __________ PERIOD __________

8-5 Word Problem Practice

Angles of Elevation and Depression

1. **LIGHTHOUSES** Sailors on a ship at sea spot the light from a lighthouse. The angle of elevation to the light is 25°.

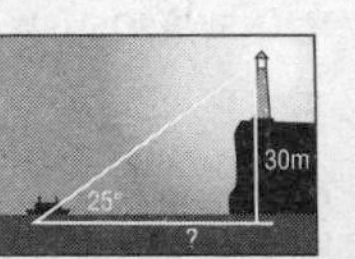

The light of the lighthouse is 30 meters above sea level. How far from the shore is the ship? Round your answer to the nearest meter.
64 m

2. **RESCUE** A hiker dropped his backpack over one side of a canyon onto a ledge below. Because of the shape of the cliff, he could not see exactly where it landed.

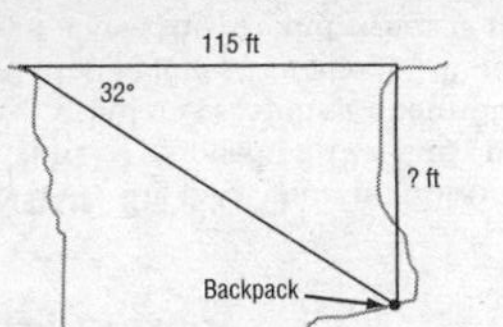

From the other side, the park ranger reports that the angle of depression to the backpack is 32°. If the width of the canyon is 115 feet, how far down did the backpack fall? Round your answer to the nearest foot.
72 ft

3. **AIRPLANES** The angle of elevation to an airplane viewed from the control tower at an airport is 7°. The tower is 200 feet high and the pilot reports that the altitude is 5200 feet. How far away from the control tower is the airplane? Round your answer to the nearest foot.
41,028 ft

4. **PEAK TRAM** The Peak Tram in Hong Kong connects two terminals, one at the base of a mountain, and the other at the summit. The angle of elevation of the upper terminal from the lower terminal is about 15.5°. The distance between the two terminals is about 1365 meters. About how much higher above sea level is the upper terminal compared to the lower terminal? Round your answer to the nearest meter.
365 m

5. **HELICOPTERS** Jermaine and John are watching a helicopter hover above the ground.

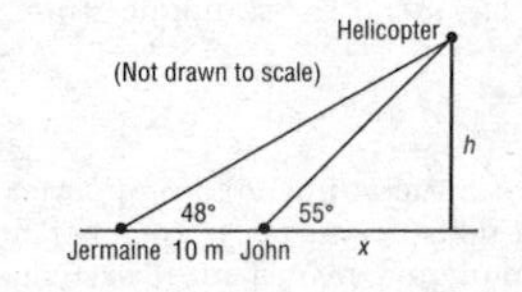

Jermaine and John are standing 10 meters apart.

a. Find two different expressions that can be used to find the h, height of the helicopter.
$h = x \tan 55°$;
$h = (x + 10) \tan 48°$

b. Equate the two expressions you found for Exercise a to solve for x. Round your answer to the nearest hundredth.
34.98 m

c. How high above the ground is the helicopter? Round your answer to the nearest hundredth.
49.95 m

NAME ______________________ DATE __________ PERIOD __________

8-5 Enrichment

Best Seat in the House

Most people want to sit in the best seat in the movie theater. The best seat could be defined as the seat that allows you to see the maximum amount of screen. The picture below represents this situation.

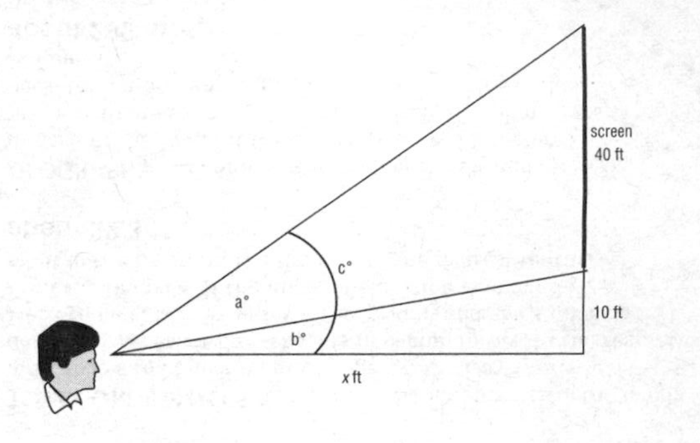

To determine the best seat in the house, you want to find what value of x allows you to see the maximum amount of screen. The value of x is how far from the screen you should sit.

1. To maximize the amount of screen viewed, which angle value needs to be maximized? Why?
Angle with measure *a* because this is how much of the screen can be viewed.

2. What is the value of a if $x = 10$ feet?
33.7 ft

3. What is the value of a if $x = 20$ feet?
41.6 ft

4. What is the value of a if $x = 25$ feet?
41.6 ft

5. What is the value of a if $x = 35$ feet?
39.1 ft

6. What is the value of a if $x = 55$ feet?
32 ft

7. Which value of x gives the greatest value of a? So, where is the best seat in the movie theater?
The best seat in the house is around 20–25 feet away from the screen.

NAME ____________ DATE ________ PERIOD ________

8-6 Study Guide and Intervention

The Law of Sines and Law of Cosines

The Law of Sines In any triangle, there is a special relationship between the angles of the triangle and the lengths of the sides opposite the angles.

Law of Sines	$\frac{\sin A}{a} = \frac{\sin B}{b} = \frac{\sin C}{c}$

Example 1 Find b. Round to the nearest tenth.

$\frac{\sin C}{c} = \frac{\sin B}{b}$ — Law of Sines

$\frac{\sin 45°}{30} = \frac{\sin 74°}{b}$ — $m\angle C = 45$, $c = 30$, $m\angle B = 74$

$b \sin 45° = 30 \sin 74°$ — Cross Products Property

$b = \frac{30 \sin 74°}{\sin 45°}$ — Divide each side by sin 45°.

$b \approx 40.8$ — Use a calculator.

Example 2 Find d. Round to the nearest tenth.

By the Triangle Angle-Sum Theorem, $m\angle E = 180 - (82 + 40)$ or 58.

$\frac{\sin D}{d} = \frac{\sin E}{e}$ — Law of Sines

$\frac{\sin 82°}{d} = \frac{\sin 58°}{24}$ — $m\angle D = 82$, $m\angle E = 58$, $e = 24$

$24 \sin 82° = d \sin 58°$ — Cross Products Property

$\frac{24 \sin 82°}{\sin 58°} = d$ — Divide each side by sin 58°.

$d \approx 28.0$ — Use a calculator.

Exercises

Find x. Round to the nearest tenth.

1. **18.4**
2. **26.2**
3. **18.0**
4. **7.7**
5. **12.2**
6. **30.4**

NAME ____________ DATE ________ PERIOD ________

8-6 Study Guide and Intervention *(continued)*

The Law of Sines and Law of Cosines

The Law of Cosines Another relationship between the sides and angles of any triangle is called the **Law of Cosines.** You can use the Law of Cosines if you know three sides of a triangle or if you know two sides and the included angle of a triangle.

Law of Cosines	Let $\triangle ABC$ be any triangle with a, b, and c representing the measures of the sides opposite the angles with measures A, B, and C, respectively. Then the following equations are true. $a^2 = b^2 + c^2 - 2bc \cos A$ $\quad b^2 = a^2 + c^2 - 2ac \cos B$ $\quad c^2 = a^2 + b^2 - 2ab \cos C$

Example 1 Find c. Round to the nearest tenth.

$c^2 = a^2 + b^2 - 2ab \cos C$ — Law of Cosines

$c^2 = 12^2 + 10^2 - 2(12)(10)\cos 48°$ — $a = 12$, $b = 10$, $m\angle C = 48$

$c = \sqrt{12^2 + 10^2 - 2(12)(10)\cos 48°}$ — Take the square root of each side.

$c \approx 9.1$ — Use a calculator.

Example 2 Find $m\angle A$. Round to the nearest degree.

$a^2 = b^2 + c^2 - 2bc \cos A$ — Law of Cosines

$7^2 = 5^2 + 8^2 - 2(5)(8) \cos A$ — $a = 7$, $b = 5$, $c = 8$

$49 = 25 + 64 - 80 \cos A$ — Multiply.

$-40 = -80 \cos A$ — Subtract 89 from each side.

$\frac{1}{2} = \cos A$ — Divide each side by −80.

$\cos^{-1} \frac{1}{2} = A$ — Use the inverse cosine.

$60° = A$ — Use a calculator.

Exercises

Find x. Round angle measures to the nearest degree and side measures to the nearest tenth.

1. **13.5**
2. **51**
3. **42**
4. **29.8**
5. **24.3**
6. **53**

Lesson 8-6

Answers

NAME ______________ DATE ________ PERIOD ________

8-6 Skills Practice

The Law of Sines and Law of Cosines

Find x. Round angle measures to the nearest degree and side lengths to the nearest tenth.

1. **21.6** 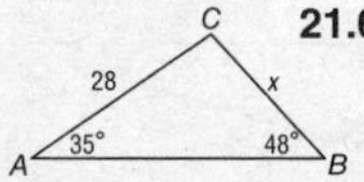
2. **7.3** 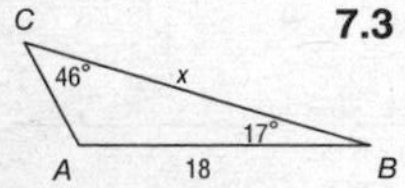
3. **48.8** 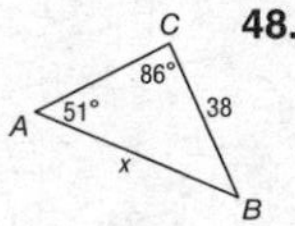
4. **16.8** 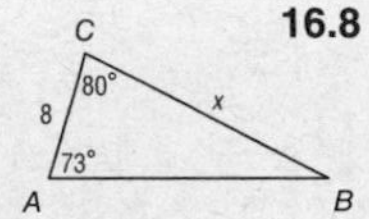
5. **43.7** 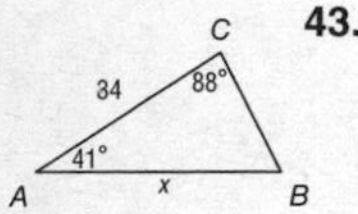
6. **19.8** 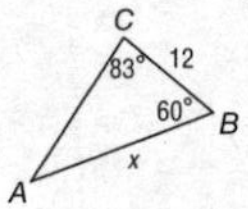
7. **46.6** 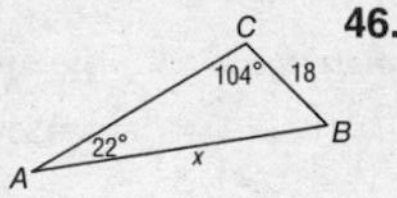
8. **40.1** 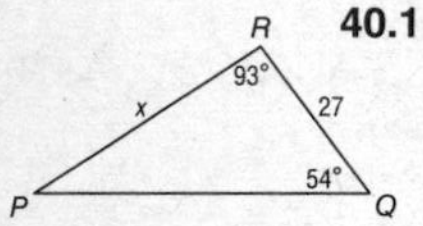
9. **88** 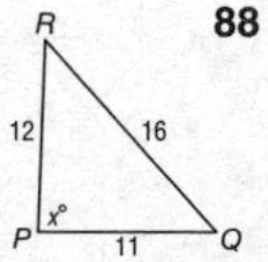
10. **52** 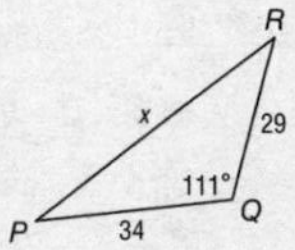
11. **19.8** 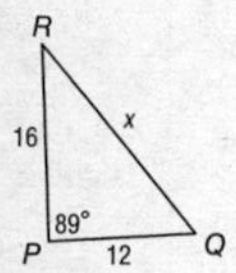
12. **26.2** 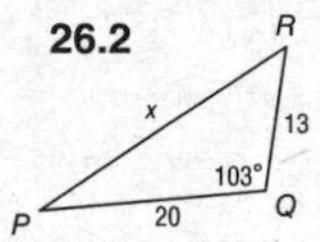
13. **38.6** 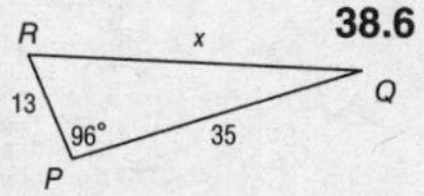
14. **67** 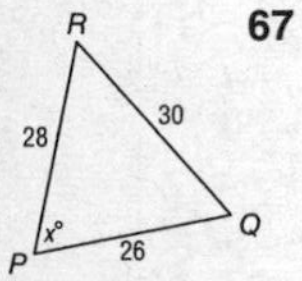
15. **11.9**

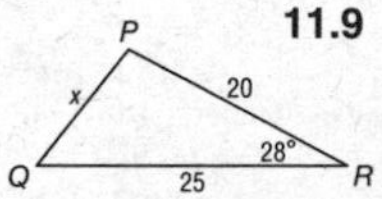

16. Solve the triangle. Round angle measures to the nearest degree.

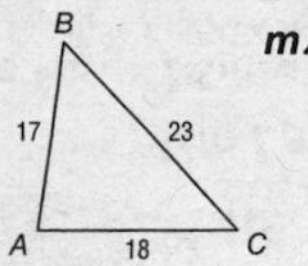

$m\angle A = 82$, $m\angle B = 51$, $m\angle C = 47$

NAME ______________ DATE ________ PERIOD ________

8-6 Practice

The Law of Sines and Law of Cosines

Find x. Round angle measures to the nearest degree and side lengths to the nearest tenth.

1. **3.7**
2. **166, 0**
3. **14.2**
4. **12.9**
5. **33.2**
6. **8.3**
7. **31.3**
8. **16.9**
9. **16.6**
10. **48**
11. **20.3**
12. **43**

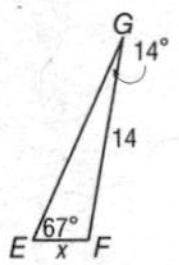

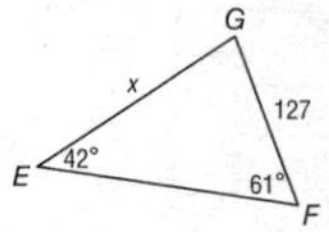

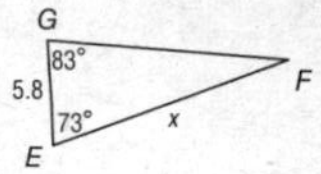

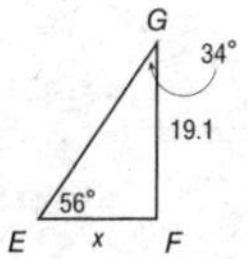

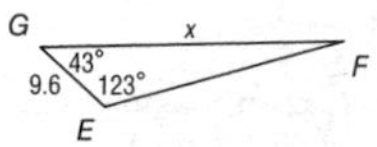

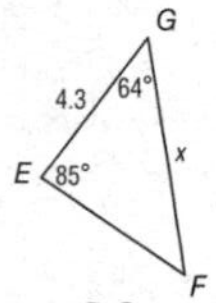

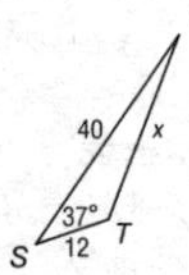

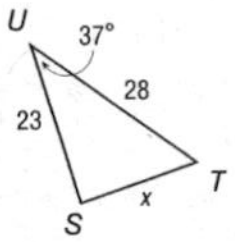

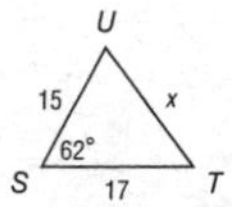

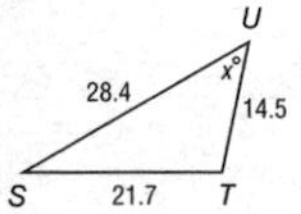

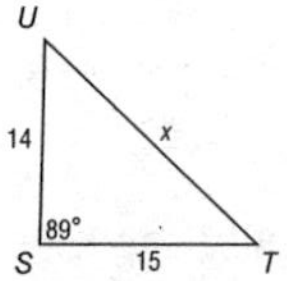

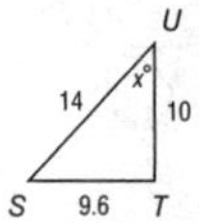

13. **INDIRECT MEASUREMENT** To find the distance from the edge of the lake to the tree on the island in the lake, Hannah set up a triangular configuration as shown in the diagram. The distance from location A to location B is 85 meters. The measures of the angles at A and B are 51° and 83°, respectively. What is the distance from the edge of the lake at B to the tree on the island at C? **about 91.8 m**

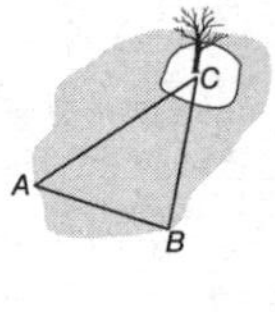

NAME ______________ DATE ________ PERIOD ________

8-6 Word Problem Practice

The Law of Sines and Law of Cosines

1. ALTITUDES In triangle ABC, the altitude to side $\overline{AB}$ is drawn.

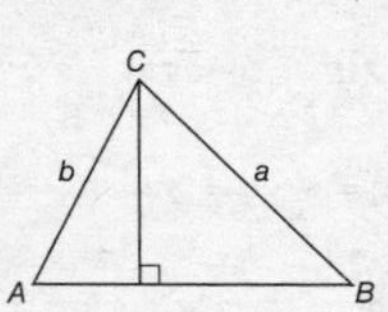

Give two expressions for the length of the altitude in terms of a, b, and the sine of the angles A and B.

a sin B = b sin A = length of altitude

2. MAPS Three cities form the vertices of a triangle. The angles of the triangle are 40°, 60°, and 80°. The two most distant cities are 40 miles apart. How close are the two closest cities? Round your answer to the nearest tenth of a mile.

26.1 mi

3. STATUES Gail was visiting an art gallery. In one room, she stood so that she had a view of two statues, one of a man, and the other of a woman. She was 40 feet from the statue of the woman, and 35 feet from the statue of the man. The angle created by the lines of sight to the two statues was 21°. What is the distance between the two statues? Round your answer to the nearest tenth.

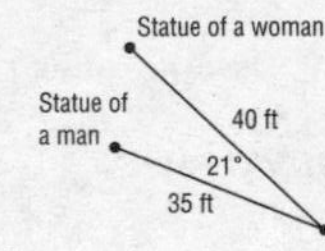

14.5 ft

4. CARS Two cars start moving from the same location. They head straight, but in different directions. The angle between where they are heading is 43°. The first car travels 20 miles and the second car travels 37 miles. How far apart are the two cars? Round your answer to the nearest tenth.

26.2 mi

5. ISLANDS Oahu is a Hawaiian Island. Off of the coast of Oahu, there is a very tiny island known as Chinaman's Hat. Keoki and Malia are observing Chinaman's Hat from locations 5 kilometers apart. Use the information in the figure to answer the following questions.

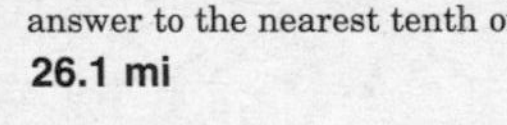

a. How far is Keoki from Chinaman's Hat? Round your answer to the nearest tenth of a kilometer.

2.0 km

b. How far is Malia from Chinaman's Hat? Round your answer to the nearest tenth of a kilometer.

4.0 km

NAME ______________ DATE ________ PERIOD ________

8-6 Enrichment

Identities

An **identity** is an equation that is true for all values of the variable for which both sides are defined. One way to verify an identity is to use a right triangle and the definitions for trigonometric functions.

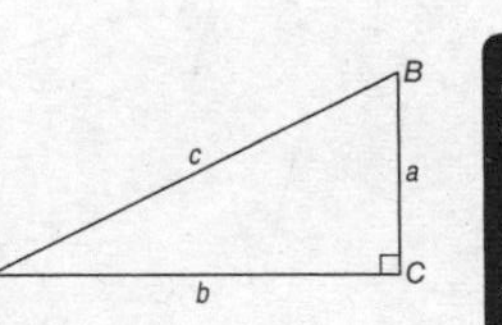

Example 1 **Verify that $(\sin A)^2 + (\cos A)^2 = 1$ is an identity.**

$$(\sin A)^2 + (\cos A)^2 = \left(\frac{a}{c}\right)^2 + \left(\frac{b}{c}\right)^2$$
$$= \frac{a^2 + b^2}{c^2} = \frac{c^2}{c^2} = 1$$

To check whether an equation *may* be an identity, you can test several values. However, since you cannot test all values, you cannot be *certain* that the equation is an identity.

Example 2 **Test $\sin 2x = 2 \sin x \cos x$ to see if it could be an identity.**

Try $x = 20$. Use a calculator to evaluate each expression.

$\sin 2x = \sin 40$
≈ 0.643

$2 \sin x \cos x = 2 (\sin 20)(\cos 20)$
$\approx 2(0.342)(0.940)$
≈ 0.643

Since the left and right sides seem equal, the equation may be an identity.

Exercises

Use triangle ABC shown above. Verify that each equation is an identity.

1. $\frac{\cos A}{\sin A} = \frac{1}{\tan A}$

$$\frac{\cos A}{\sin A} = \frac{b}{c} \div \frac{a}{c} = \frac{b}{a} = \frac{1}{\tan A}$$

2. $\frac{\tan B}{\sin B} = \frac{1}{\cos B}$

$$\frac{\tan B}{\sin B} = \frac{b}{a} \div \frac{b}{c} = \frac{c}{a} = \frac{1}{\cos B}$$

3. $\tan B \cos B = \sin B$

$$\tan B \cos B = \frac{b}{a} \cdot \frac{a}{c} = \frac{b}{c} = \sin B$$

4. $1 - (\cos B)^2 = (\sin B)^2$

$$1 - (\cos B)^2 = 1 - \left(\frac{a}{c}\right)^2 = \frac{c^2}{c^2} - \frac{a^2}{c^2} = \frac{c^2 - a^2}{c^2} = \frac{b^2}{c^2} \text{ or } (\sin B)^2$$

Try several values for x to test whether each equation could be an identity.

5. $\cos 2x = (\cos x)^2 - (\sin x)^2$

Yes; see students' work.

6. $\cos (90 - x) = \sin x$

Yes; see students' work.

NAME ______________ DATE ________ PERIOD ________

8-6 Graphing Calculator Activity

Solving Triangles Using the Law of Sines or Cosines

You can use a calculator to solve triangles using the Law of Sines or Cosines.

Example **Solve $\triangle ABC$ if $a = 6$, $b = 2$, and $c = 7.5$.**

Use the Law of Cosines.

$a^2 = b^2 + c^2 - 2bc \cos A$

$6^2 = 2^2 + 7.5^2 - 2(2)(7.5) \cos A$

$m\angle A = \cos^{-1} \frac{6^2 - 2^2 - 7.5^2}{-2(2)(7.5)}$ Use your calculator to find the measure of $\angle A$.

Keystrokes: [2nd] [COS⁻¹] [(] 6 [x²] [−] 2 [x²] [−] 7.5 [x²] [)] [÷] [(] [(−)] 2 [×] 2 [×] 7.5 [)] [)] [ENTER] 36.06658826

So $m\angle A \approx 36$. Use the Law of Sines and your calculator to find $m\angle B$.

$\frac{\sin A}{a} = \frac{\sin B}{b}$

$\frac{\sin 36}{6} \approx \frac{\sin B}{2}$

$m\angle B \approx \sin^{-1} \frac{2 \sin 36°}{6}$

Keystrokes: [2nd] [SIN⁻¹] [(] 2 [SIN] 36 [)] [÷] 6 [)] [ENTER] 11.29896425

So $m\angle B \approx 11$. By the Triangle Angle-Sum Theorem, $m\angle C \approx 180 - (36 + 11)$ or 133.

Exercises

Solve each $\triangle ABC$. Round measures of sides to the nearest tenth and measures of angles to the nearest degree.

1. $a = 9, b = 14, c = 12$ ***$m\angle A \approx 40$, $m\angle B \approx 89$, $m\angle C \approx 51$***

2. $m\angle C = 80, c = 9, m\angle A = 40$ ***$m\angle B = 60$, $a \approx 5.9$, $b \approx 7.9$***

3. $m\angle B = 45, m\angle C = 56, a = 2$ ***$m\angle A = 79$, $b \approx 1.4$, $c \approx 1.7$***

4. $a = 5.7, b = 6, c = 5$ ***$m\angle A = 62$, $m\angle B = 68$, $m\angle C = 50$***

5. $a = 11, b = 15, c = 21$ ***$m\angle A \approx 30$, $m\angle B \approx 43$, $m\angle C \approx 107$***

NAME ______________ DATE ________ PERIOD ________

8-7 Study Guide and Intervention

Vectors

Geometric Vector Operations A vector is a directed segment representing a quantity that has both **magnitude,** or length, and **direction.** For example, the speed and direction of an airplane can be represented by a vector. In symbols, a vector is written as $\overrightarrow{AB}$, where A is the initial point and B is the endpoint, or as $\vec{v}$. The sum of two vectors is called the **resultant.** Subtracting a vector is equivalent to adding its opposite. The resultant of two vectors can be found using the **parallelogram method** or the **triangle method.**

Example **Copy the vectors to find $\vec{a} - \vec{b}$.**

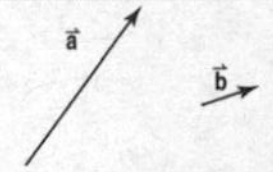

Method 1: Use the parallelogram method.

Copy $\vec{a}$ and $-\vec{b}$ with the same initial point. 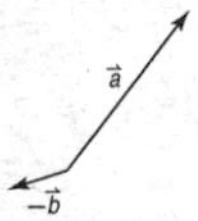	Complete the parallelogram. 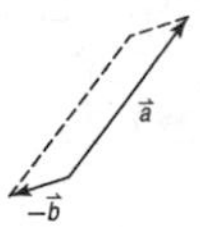	Draw the diagonal of the parallelogram from the initial point. 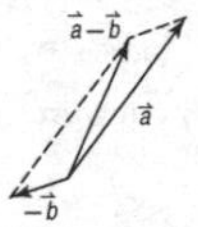

Method 2: Use the triangle method.

Copy $\vec{a}$. 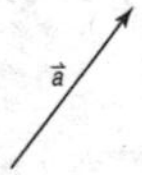	Place the initial point of $-\vec{b}$ at the terminal point of $\vec{a}$. 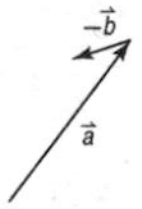	Draw the vector from the initial point of $\vec{a}$ to the terminal point of $-\vec{b}$. 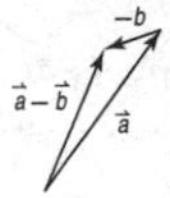

Exercises

Copy the vectors. Then find each sum or difference.

1. $\vec{c} + \vec{d}$

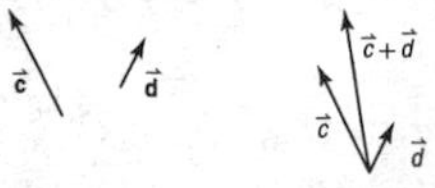

2. $\vec{w} - \vec{z}$

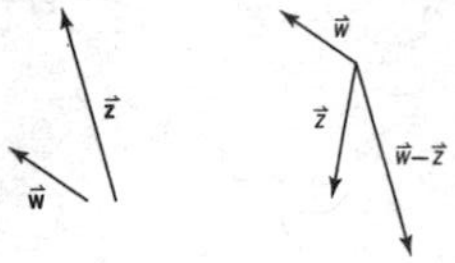

3. $\vec{a} - \vec{b}$

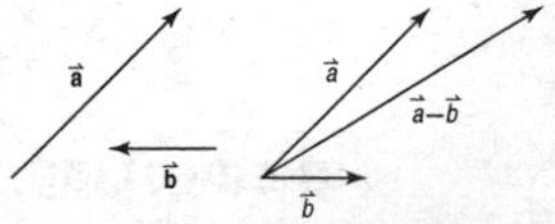

4. $\vec{r} + \vec{t}$

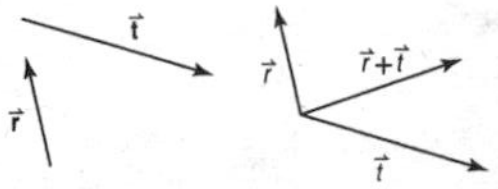

NAME ______________ DATE ________ PERIOD ________

8-7 Study Guide and Intervention *(continued)*

Vectors

Vectors on the Coordinate Plane A vector in **standard position** has its initial point at (0, 0) and can be represented by the ordered pair for point B. The vector at the right can be expressed as $\vec{v} = \langle 5, 3 \rangle$. You can use the Distance Formula to find the magnitude $|\overline{AB}|$ of a vector. You can describe the direction of a vector by measuring the angle that the vector forms with the positive x-axis or with any other horizontal line.

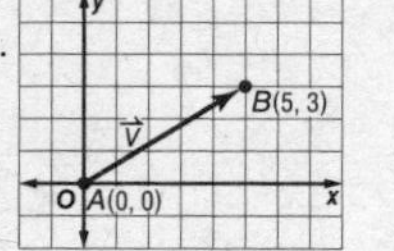

Example **Find the magnitude and direction of $\vec{a} = \langle 3, 5 \rangle$.**

Find the magnitude.

$\vec{a} = \sqrt{(x_2 - x_1)^2 + (y_2 - y_1)^2}$ — Distance Formula

$= \sqrt{(3 - 0)^2 + (5 - 0)^2}$ — $(x_1, y_1) = (0, 0)$ and $(x_2, y_2) = (3, 5)$

$= \sqrt{34}$ or about 5.8 — Simplify.

To find the direction, use the tangent ratio.

$\tan \theta = \frac{5}{3}$ — The tangent ratio is opposite over adjacent.

$m\angle\theta \approx 59.0$ — Use a calculator.

The magnitude of the vector is about 5.8 units and its direction is 59°.

Exercises

Find the magnitude and direction of each vector.

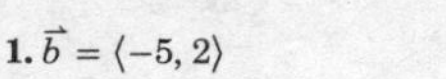

1. $\vec{b} = \langle -5, 2 \rangle$ **5.4; 158.2°**
2. $\vec{c} = \langle -2, 1 \rangle$ **2.2; 153.4°**
3. $\vec{d} = \langle 3, 4 \rangle$ **5; 53.1°**
4. $\vec{m} = \langle 5, -1 \rangle$ **5.1; 348.7°**
5. $\vec{r} = \langle -3, -4 \rangle$ **5; 233.1°**
6. $\vec{v} = \langle -4, 1 \rangle$ **4.1; 166.0°**

NAME ______________ DATE ________ PERIOD ________

8-7 Skills Practice

Vectors

Use a ruler and a protractor to draw each vector. Include a scale on each diagram.

1. $\vec{a}$ = 20 meters per second 60° west of south
2. $\vec{b}$ = 10 pound of force at 135° to the horizontal

Copy the vectors to find each sum or difference.

3. $\vec{a} + \vec{z}$
4. $\vec{t} - \vec{r}$

Write the component form of each vector.

5. **⟨3, 4⟩**

6.

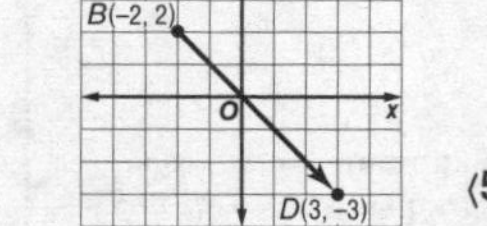

⟨5, −5⟩

Find the magnitude and direction of each vector.

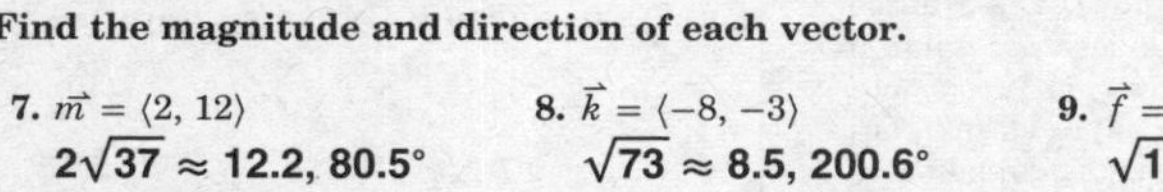

7. $\vec{m} = \langle 2, 12 \rangle$ **$2\sqrt{37} \approx 12.2$, 80.5°**
8. $\vec{k} = \langle -8, -3 \rangle$ **$\sqrt{73} \approx 8.5$, 200.6°**
9. $\vec{f} = \langle -5, 11 \rangle$ **$\sqrt{146} \approx 12.1$, 155.6°**

Find each of the following for $\vec{a} = \langle 2, 4 \rangle$, $\vec{b} = \langle 3, -3 \rangle$, and $\vec{c} = \langle 4, -1 \rangle$. Check your answers graphically.

10. $2\vec{a} + \vec{b}$ **⟨7, 5⟩**
11. $\vec{b} - 2\vec{c}$ **⟨−5, −1⟩**

NAME ____________ DATE ________ PERIOD ________

8-7 Practice

Vectors

Use a ruler and a protractor to draw each vector. Include a scale on each diagram.

1. $\vec{v}$ = 12 Newtons of force at 40° to the horizontal

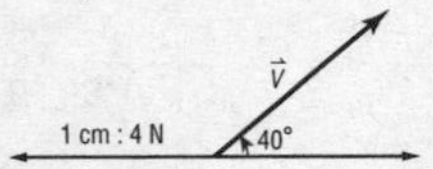

1 cm : 4 N

2. $\vec{w}$ = 15 miles per hour 70° east of north

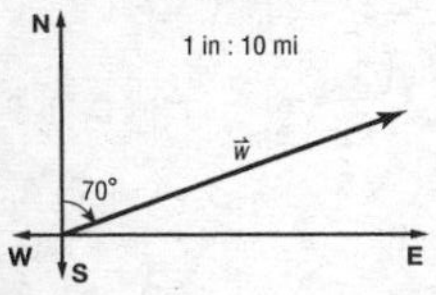

1 in : 10 mi

Copy the vectors to find each sum or difference.

3. $\vec{p} + \vec{r}$

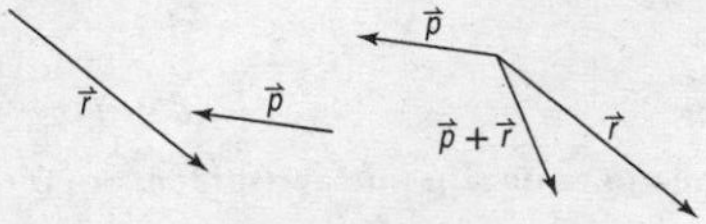

4. $\vec{a} - \vec{b}$

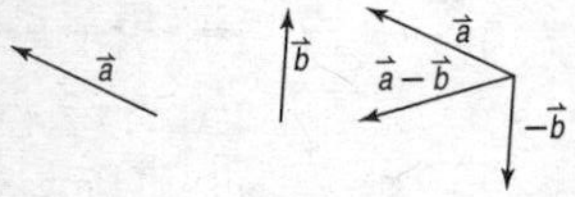

5. Write the component form of $\overrightarrow{AB}$.

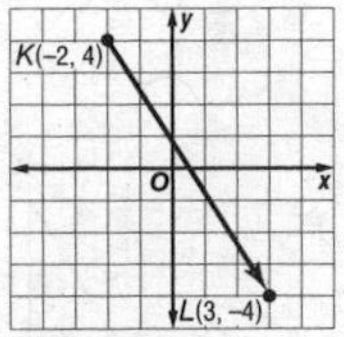

K(−2, 4), L(3, −4)

⟨5, −8⟩

Find the magnitude and direction of each vector.

6. $\vec{t}$ = ⟨6, 11⟩

7. $\vec{g}$ = ⟨9, −7⟩

Find each of the following for $\vec{a}$ = ⟨−1.5, 4⟩, $\vec{b}$ = ⟨7, 3⟩, and $\vec{c}$ = ⟨1, −2⟩. Check your answers graphically.

8. $2\vec{a} + \vec{b}$ **⟨−1, 13⟩**

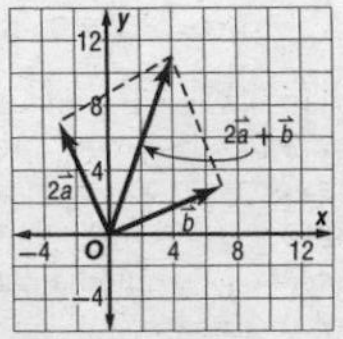

9. $2\vec{c} - \vec{b}$ **⟨−5, −1⟩**

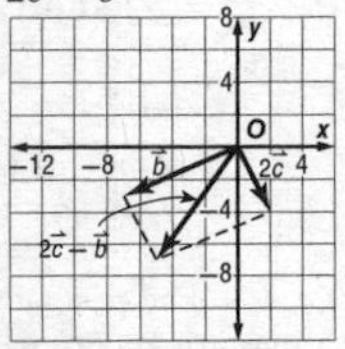

10. **AVIATION** A jet begins a flight along a path due north at 300 miles per hour. A wind is blowing due west at 30 miles per hour.

a. Find the resultant velocity of the plane. **about 301.5 mph**

b. Find the resultant direction of the plane. **about 5.7° west of due north**

NAME ____________ DATE ________ PERIOD ________

8-7 Word Problem Practice

Vectors

1. **WIND** The vector $\vec{v}$ represents the speed and direction that the wind is blowing. Suddenly the wind picks up and doubles its speed, but the direction does not change. Write an expression for a vector that describes the new wind velocity in terms of $\vec{v}$.

$2\vec{v}$

2. **SWIMMING** Jan is swimming in a triathlon event. When the ocean water is still, her velocity can be represented by the vector ⟨2, 1⟩ miles per hour. During the competition, there was a fierce current represented by the vector ⟨−1, −1⟩ miles per hour. What vector represents Jan's velocity during the race?

⟨1, 0⟩ mph

3. **POLYGONS** Draw a regular polygon around the origin. For each side of the polygon, associate a vector whose magnitude is the length of the corresponding side and whose direction points in the clockwise motion around the origin. What vector represents the sum of all these vectors? Explain.

⟨0, 0⟩; Because the polygon forms a closed loop, the sum is the zero vector.

4. **BASEBALL** Rick is in the middle of a baseball game. His teammate throws him the ball, but throws it far in front of him. He has to run as fast as he can to catch it. As he runs, he knows that as soon as he catches it, he has to throw it as hard as he can to the teammate at home plate. He has no time to stop. In the figure, $\vec{x}$ is the vector that represents the velocity of the ball *after* Rick throws it and $\vec{v}$ represents Rick's velocity because he is running. Assume that Rick can throw just as hard when running as he can when standing still.

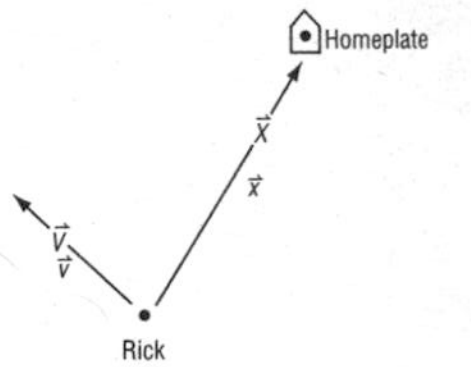

Homeplate, Rick

a. What vector would represent the velocity of the ball if Rick threw it the same way but he was standing still?

$\vec{x} - \vec{v}$

b. The angle between $\vec{x}$ and $\vec{v}$ is 89°. By running, did it help Rick get the ball to home plate faster than he would have normally been able to if he were standing still?

Yes, it helped.

NAME ______________________ DATE __________ PERIOD ________

8-7 Enrichment

Dot Product

The dot product of two vectors represents how much the vectors point in the direction of each other. If $\vec{v}$ is a vector represented by $\langle a, b\rangle$ and $\vec{u}$ is a vector represented by $\langle c, d\rangle$, the formula to find the dot product is:

$\vec{v} \cdot \vec{u} = ac + bd$

Look at the following example:

Graph the vectors and find the dot product of $\vec{v}$ and $\vec{u}$ if
$\vec{v} = \langle 3, -1\rangle$ and $\vec{u} = \langle 2, 5\rangle$.
$\vec{v} \cdot \vec{u} = (3)(2) + (-1)(5)$ or 1

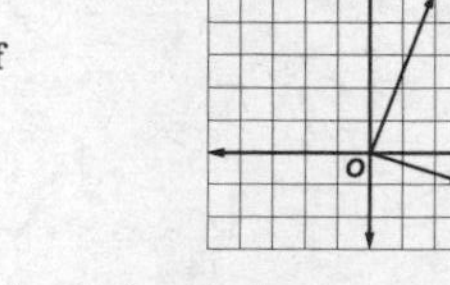

Graph the vectors and find the dot products.

1. $\vec{v} = \langle 2, 1\rangle$ and $\vec{u} = \langle -4, 2\rangle$
The dot product is **−6**

2. $\vec{v} = \langle 3, -2\rangle$ and $\vec{u} = \langle 1, 4\rangle$
The dot product is **−5**

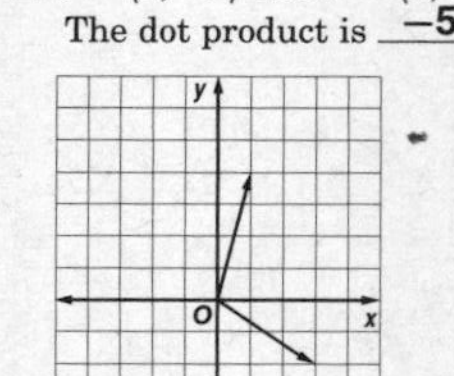

3. $\vec{v} = \langle 0, 3\rangle$ and $\vec{u} = \langle 2, 4\rangle$
The dot product is **12**

4. $\vec{v} = \langle -1, 4\rangle$ and $\vec{u} = \langle -4, 2\rangle$
The dot product is **12**

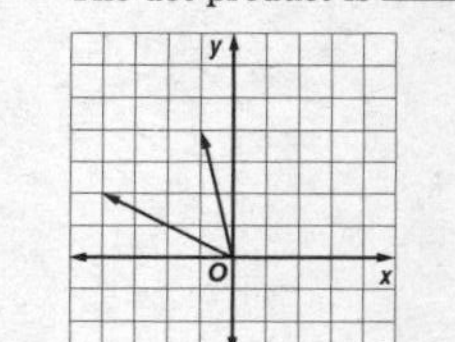

5. Notice the angle formed by the two vectors and the corresponding dot product. Is there any relationship between the type of angle between the two vectors and the sign of the dot product? Make a conjecture.

Yes, there is a relationship between the type of angle between the two vectors and the sign of the dot product. When the angle formed is acute, the sign of the dot product is positive and when the angle formed is obtuse, the sign of the dot product is negative.

Answers

Chapter 8 Assessment Answer Key

Quiz 1 (Lessons 8-1 and 8-2)
Page 51

1. $8\sqrt{3}$
2. $x = \sqrt{85}$, $y = 2\sqrt{15}$
3. $x = \sqrt{17}$, $y = \frac{81}{8}$
4. $\sqrt{137}$
5. acute

Quiz 2 (Lessons 8-3 and 8-4)
Page 51

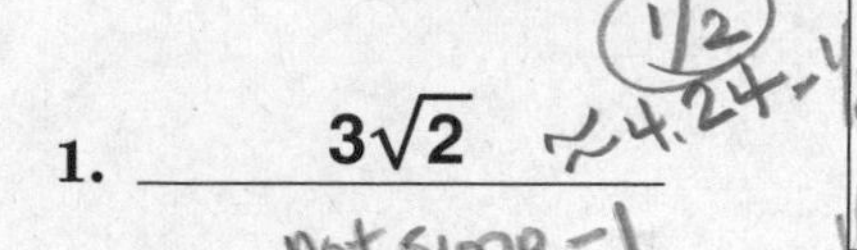

1. $3\sqrt{2}$
2. $2\sqrt{3}$
3. 57.8
4. 14.6
5. $20\sqrt{3} + 20$ in.
6. 0.7880
7. 27
8. 3.3 ft
9. 27.1
10. 22.0

Quiz 3 (Lessons 8-5 and 8-6)
Page 52

1. $\angle QPR$
2. 3.9
3. $m\angle B = 104$, $m\angle C = 27$, $b = 23.2$
4. $m\angle R = 88$, $m\angle T = 53$, $m\angle S = 39$
5. 52°

Quiz 4 (Lesson 8-7)
Page 52

1. 24.8 units, 220°
2. 31.4 units, 158°
3. 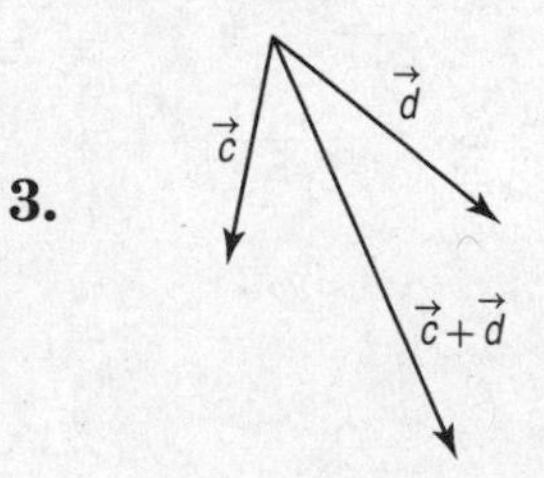

4. 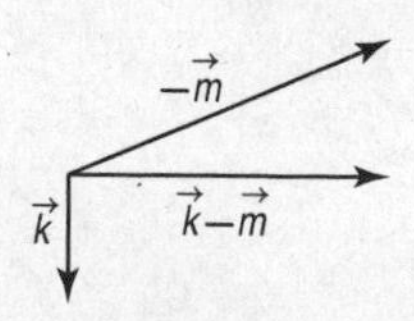

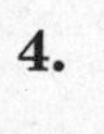
5. 6 mph, south

Mid-Chapter Test
Page 53

Part I

1. A
2. H
3. B
4. H
5. D

Part II

6. $x = 9$, $y = 3\sqrt{3}$
7. $x = 10\sqrt{3}$, $y = 10\sqrt{6}$
8. $x = 12\sqrt{2}$, $y = 24\sqrt{2}$
9. right
10. 54

Answers

Chapter 8 Assessment Answer Key

Vocabulary Test
Page 54

1. geometric mean
2. Pythagorean triple
3. false, trigonometric ratio
4. true
5. angle of depression
6. trigonometry
7. sine
8. tangent
9. A method to describe a vector using its horizontal and vertical change from its inital to terminal point.
10. In a right triangle, the sum of the squares of the measures of the legs equals the square of the measure of the hypotenuse.

Form 1
Page 55

1. D
2. F
3. A
4. G
5. D
6. G
7. C
8. G
9. C
10. H

Page 56

11. C
12. F
13. A
14. G
15. D
16. F
17. B
18. F
19. C
20. G

B: 69

Chapter 8 Assessment Answer Key

Form 2A

Page 57

1. D
2. J
3. A
4. H
5. D
6. J
7. A
8. G
9. B
10. H

Page 58

11. B
12. F
13. C
14. G
15. D
16. H
17. C
18. G
19. D
20. H

B: 56.4 ft

Form 2B

Page 59

1. A
2. J
3. D
4. G
5. D
6. F
7. A
8. H
9. B
10. H

Page 60

11. B
12. H
13. C
14. G
15. D
16. G
17. A
18. G
19. B
20. J

B: 73.2 ft

Answers

Chapter 8 Assessment Answer Key

Form 2C
Page 61

1. $\sqrt{10}$
2. 13
3. $2\sqrt{7}$
4. $\sqrt{4000}$ or $20\sqrt{10}$
5. $\sqrt{300}$ or $10\sqrt{3}$
6. $11\sqrt{2}$
7. $2\sqrt{3}$
8. $x = 6, y = 12$
9. 9.7
10. 69
11. 68

Page 62

12. 267.9m
13. 11°
14. 43.2
15. 14.3
16. 15.6 ft
17. 20
18. 33.0
19. $\sqrt{170} \approx 13$ units; 237.5°
20. $\vec{s}$, $\vec{s}+\vec{t}$, $\vec{t}$

B: 1

Chapter 8 Assessment Answer Key

Form 2D

Page 63

1. 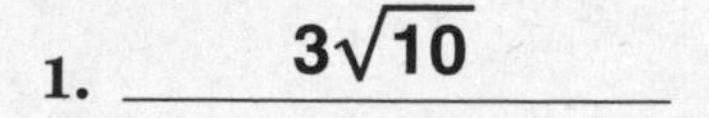

2. 26

3. $\sqrt{39}$

4. $\sqrt{7300}$ or $10\sqrt{73}$

5. $\sqrt{432}$ or $12\sqrt{3}$

6. $15\sqrt{2}$

7. $7\sqrt{3}$

8. $x = 12, y = 24$

9. 8.6

10. 70°

11. 67°

Page 64

12. 352.7 m

13. 9°

14. 32.3

15. 6.2°

16. 15.2 ft

17. 19

18. 38.2

19. $\sqrt{109} \approx 10.4$ units, 253.3°

20. $-\vec{f}$, $\vec{d} - \vec{f}$, $\vec{d}$

B: 6 or 10

Answers

Chapter 8 Assessment Answer Key

Form 3
Page 65

1. $\frac{\sqrt{6}}{9}$
2. 2
3. 3
4. $2\sqrt{10}$
5. $\frac{12}{5}$
6. 12.5
7. 250 km
8. right
9. $12\sqrt{6}$
10. $24 + 8\sqrt{3}$
11. $x = 5\sqrt{3}$, $y = 10\sqrt{3}$
12. $(-4 + 8\sqrt{3}, -2)$ or $(-4 - 8\sqrt{3}, -2)$

Page 66

13. $x = \frac{5\sqrt{6}}{3}$, $CD = 5\frac{\sqrt{6}}{3} + 5\sqrt{2} + 12$
14. 147 ft
15. 2 ft
16. 37.4
17. 253.7 yd
18. 37° or 143°
19. 31.4 units, 261°

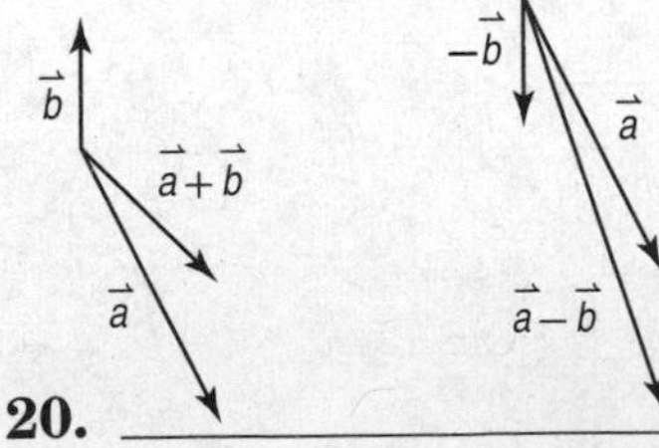

20.

B: 71.1 ft and 84.5 ft

Chapter 8 Assessment Answer Key

Extended-Response Test, Page 67
Scoring Rubric

Score	General Description	Specific Criteria
4	**Superior** A correct solution that is supported by well-developed, accurate explanations	• Shows thorough understanding of the concepts of *geometric mean*, *special right triangles*, *altitude to the hypotenuse theorems*, *Pythagorean Theorem*, *solving triangles*, *SOH CAH TOA*, *Law of Sines*, and *Law of Cosines*. • Uses appropriate strategies to solve problems. • Computations are correct. • Written explanations are exemplary. • Figures are accurate and appropriate. • Goes beyond requirements of some or all problems.
3	**Satisfactory** A generally correct solution, but may contain minor flaws in reasoning or computation	• Shows an understanding of the concepts of *geometric mean*, *special right triangles*, *altitude to the hypotenuse theorems*, *Pythagorean Theorem*, *solving triangles*, *SOH CAH TOA*, *Law of Sines*, and *Law of Cosines*. • Uses appropriate strategies to solve problems. • Computations are mostly correct. • Written explanations are effective. • Figures are mostly accurate and appropriate. • Satisfies all requirements of problems.
2	**Nearly Satisfactory** A partially correct interpretation and/or solution to the problem	• Shows an understanding of most of the concepts of *geometric mean*, *special right triangles*, *altitude to the hypotenuse theorems*, *Pythagorean Theorem*, *solving triangles*, *SOH CAH TOA*, *Law of Sines* and *Law of Cosines*. • May not use appropriate strategies to solve problems. • Computations are mostly correct. • Written explanations are satisfactory. • Figures are mostly accurate. • Satisfies the requirements of most of the problems.
1	**Nearly Unsatisfactory** A correct solution with no supporting evidence or explanation	• Final computation is correct. • No written explanations or work is shown to substantiate the final computation. • Figures may be accurate but lack detail or explanation. • Satisfies minimal requirements of some of the problems.
0	**Unsatisfactory** An incorrect solution indicating no mathematical understanding of the concept or task, or no solution is given	• Shows little or no understanding of most of the concepts of *geometric mean*, *special right triangles*, *altitude to the hypotenuse theorems*, *Pythagorean Theorem*, *solving triangles*, *SOH CAH TOA*, *Law of Sines* and *Law of Cosines*. • Does not use appropriate strategies to solve problems. • Computations are incorrect. • Written explanations are unsatisfactory. • Figures are inaccurate or inappropriate. • Does not satisfy requirements of problems. • No answer given.

Answers

Chapter 8 Assessment Answer Key

Extended-Response Test, Page 67
Sample Answers

In addition to the scoring rubric found on page A31, the following sample answers may be used as guidance in evaluating open-ended assessment items.

1. $\frac{10}{6} = \frac{6}{x}$

$10x = 36$

$x = \frac{18}{5}$

2a. No, his work is not correct. The triangle is not a right triangle so he cannot use the altitude to the hypotenuse theorem. Instead he must use the 30°-60°-90° triangle relationships and obtain $x = 2\sqrt{3}$.

b. Using the 30°-60°-90° triangle relationships, $RQ = 4$, and therefore PQ would have to equal 8, so $PS = 8 - 2$ or 6.

c. No, the sides are not in a ratio of $1:1:\sqrt{2}$.

3. If you were finding the length of a side x you would use *sin* of the given angle. If you are finding an angle x you would use the sin^{-1} of the ratio of two sides to find the angle. For example, if $sin\ x = \frac{3}{4}$, use $sin^{-1}\frac{3}{4}$ to find x. If $sin\ 20° = \frac{x}{5}$ find the sine of 20° and multiply by 5 to find x, the length of the unknown side.

4.

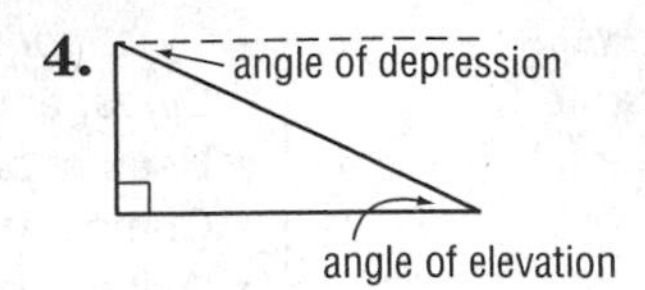

Student should draw a right triangle and label the angle of elevation up from the horizontal and the angle of depression down from the horizontal. The angle of elevation has the same measure as the angle of depression.

5.

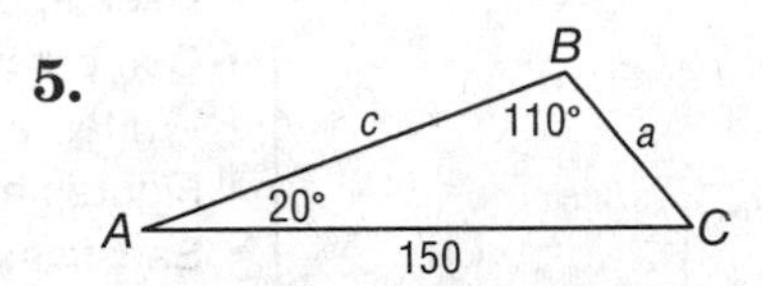

Let $m\angle B = 110$, $m\angle A = 20$, and $b = 150$. Use the Law of Sines to find the missing lengths. The length of a is found using $\frac{\sin 110°}{150} = \frac{\sin 20°}{a}$. The third angle is found by evaluating $180 - (m\angle B + m\angle A)$. In this problem, $m\angle C = 50$. The length of c is found by using $\frac{\sin 110°}{150} = \frac{\sin 50°}{c}$.

In this problem, $c \approx 122.3$.

6. No, her plan is not a good one. Irina should use the Law of Cosines to find angle B. Then she can use the Law of Sines to find either angle A or angle C and subtract the two angles she finds from 180 degrees to get the measure of the third angle.

Chapter 8 Assessment Answer Key

Standardized Test Practice
Page 68

1. ● Ⓑ Ⓒ Ⓓ

2. ● Ⓖ Ⓗ Ⓙ

3. Ⓐ Ⓑ ● Ⓓ

4. Ⓕ Ⓖ Ⓗ ●

5. Ⓐ Ⓑ Ⓒ ●

6. Ⓕ ● Ⓗ Ⓙ

7. Ⓐ Ⓑ Ⓒ ●

8. Ⓕ ● Ⓗ Ⓙ

9. Ⓐ Ⓑ Ⓒ ●

Page 69

10. Ⓕ Ⓖ Ⓗ ●

11. Ⓐ ● Ⓒ Ⓓ

12. Ⓕ Ⓖ Ⓗ ●

13. Ⓐ Ⓑ ● Ⓓ

14. Ⓕ ● Ⓗ Ⓙ

15.

1	4	.	5	

16.

1	8	.	0	

Answers

Chapter 8 Assessment Answer Key

Standardized Practice Test
Page 70

17. Def. of ≅ segments

18. $HJ + JK = HK$; $KL + LM = KM$

19. $m\angle 1 = 32$, $m\angle 2 = 82$, $m\angle 3 = 66$, $m\angle 4 = 114$, $m\angle 5 = 57$

20. 7

21. 19

22. $\angle 3$, $\angle 4$, $\angle 5$, $\angle 7$, $\angle ABC$

23a. yes, both are 30°- 60°- 90° triangles; AA Similarity

23b. 36

23c. 2:1